THE
BIG
G
BOOK
OF
NUMBERS
THE
MAN MADE
WORLD
Elizabeth Holt

Elizabeth Holt

The Big Book of Numbers

Designed by Sarah Fretwell

Illustrated by Rod Clark

Pan Original
Pan Books London, Sydney and Auckland

First published 1990 by Pan Books Ltd,
Cavaye Place, London SW10 9PG
9 8 7 6 5 4 3 2
© Elizabeth Holt 1989
Illustrations © Rod Clark
Designed by Sarah Fretwell
ISBN 0 330 30860 2
Photoset by Parker Typesetting Service, Leicester
Printed by Clays Ltd, St Ives plc

INTRODUCTION

This book is about numbers, how they were invented and developed, and about how they can be used. They are essential. For instance, without them we could only barter, for without weights and measures and money there can be no calculation and therefore no buying or selling. Time would have very little meaning. In fact, we can't do without numbers.

That's why it is important to learn how to use them. Lots of people become depressed as soon as they are faced with figures, but there's really no need to feel like that. Just learning to think about them in a different way will help.

It's no good pretending that all sums are easy. They aren't, but by learning how to handle them and using some of the short cuts explained in this book, most people should feel a bit more confident about tackling rather more complicated problems.

The important thing to remember is that numbers didn't just happen. Man invented them, and what man invented, man can understand.

CONTENTS

Time

4 | Metrology

5 | Languages

6 | Religion

7 | Figuremania

8 Lucky and Unlucky Numbers

9 Numbers at Home

10 Numbers in Sport

I | THE HISTORY OF NUMBERS

We take figures for granted. We use them to count, to measure and to tell us how many; we use them to put things in order and we use them to calculate.

Early man didn't know about numbers. He could see for himself that an animal had 4 legs, but if he saw a large herd of deer at a watering hole, he wouldn't have been able to tell anyone else just how many there were. His fingers would have helped, but there was nothing beyond that.

We know that primitive people were aware of numbers because in some prehistoric caves there are pictures of animals with lines scratched beside them, perhaps indicating the number which someone had hunted down and killed.

The fact that man couldn't count might not have mattered much to a hunter, but as people settled down and started to farm it became very important indeed. Farmers needed to keep track of their animals, so they found ways of doing it. As they sent their herds out to graze, perhaps they dropped a pebble in a pot or put a stick on one side as each animal plodded off. Then, as each returned, a pebble was taken out or a stick removed from the pile. That would have told each farmer if any were missing. It was the beginning of mathematics.

What was needed next was a way of writing numerals, and man invented one at much the same time as he invented alphabets. By 2800 BC the Sumerians were writing wedge-shaped numerals and the Egyptians were busy working out their own system. Different civilizations developed different methods of writing and notation, the people of one country frequently adopting good ideas from another. The Romans borrowed their method of writing numerals from the Greeks, but the Greeks had already borrowed it from the Etruscans. The Egyptians used vertical strokes for numbers ranging from 1 to 4, and so did the Cretans and the Hittites. For numbers 5 to 8 or sometimes for 5 to 9, they used 2 groups of figures from the 1–4 range. For 9, 3 groups of figures were used. It was helpful, but it was also time-consuming and not very practical. So the Egyptians thought again and came up with a new idea. They used one set of signs for the numbers 1 to 10, others for multiples of 10 to 90 and for 100s to 900s, and yet another for 1,000 to 9,000. This simplified things. If they wanted to express the number 7,954 they used only 4 symbols instead of the 20 or so which would have been needed previously.

However, something was still missing from all methods of notation. It was zero, and it was probably devised in India about 1,000 years ago. Without zero no one would know the value of any other figure, whether for instance a 4 meant 4 units, 4 tens, 4 thousands or anything else. When the Babylonians worked out their system it was one of place values. They had a special sign to show that a number wasn't being used, but it was the idea of zero being an extra number that revolutionised mathematics. The word for zero in India was *sanya*, which actually meant 'empty'. The Arabs who adopted the idea translated the word literally as *sifr*, and *sifr* became zero to us. In the West and in many other parts of the world the method of writing numerals is called arabic because they were introduced into Europe by the Arabs although they originated in India. Europeans developed them between the twelfth and fifteenth centuries and gradually they elbowed out the roman numerals which everyone had used up to then.

Methods of counting

Fingers

Primitive people, just as small children do today, counted on their fingers. In some early languages the word for 5 was the same as that for hand. 10 was both hands; 20 was two men's hands.

Some used the joints of their fingers for counting, which meant that they were able to count up to 14 on each hand. Counting started from the lowest joint, so it began from the bottom of the little finger with 1, 2 and 3. Numbers 4–12 came from the joints of the next three fingers, and 13 and 14 were the bottom and top joints of the thumb.

There were variations in other areas of the world. In parts of India, Indochina, Iran and Iraq, a duodecimal system of counting was used so that people counted in twelves using the joints of 4 fingers.

Notched bones and tally sticks

We know that prehistoric man kept records by making notches on bones. Some have been discovered which are at least 20,000 years old. Using the example of the farmer again, he probably kept a tally on a bone, sometimes making a different shaped notch for higher numbers like 5 and 10.

Bones were eventually replaced by tally sticks as a method of accounting, and these were still in use in many parts of the world in the nineteenth century. This system was used by the Court of Exchequer in England to record the payment of taxes, among other things. Differently shaped notches represented pounds, shillings and pence. They were not officially abolished until 1826, but even then those which had piled up over the years weren't destroyed. It was not until 8 years later that it was decided that they should be disposed of, and quite stupidly the method chosen was burning. That in itself was not stupid, but the idea of cramming them in a stove in the House of Lords certainly was. The stove was stuffed, piles stood ready for their turn and the fire was lit, but unfortunately it wasn't only the tally sticks that burned. The wooden panelling smouldered and caught fire, the flames from the House of Lords spread to the House of Commons, and so in 1834 the Houses of Parliament were totally consumed by fire.

Knotted strings

When the Spanish reached Peru in the sixteenth century they found that the Incas kept records with knotted pieces of string. These strings were used for lots of different purposes. The distance between each knot or group of knots, their colours, size and even patterns indicated many things – taxes, the population, how many births and deaths there had been in a stated period of time, mineral and agricultural produce and so on. This method of keeping records was used elsewhere by the Greeks, Persians and Romans, and in China they were used for accounting purposes as well as recording important events. This system was in use in the Pacific islands until quite recently, and probably is still being used in some of the remoter islands.

Abacuses and counting boards

Abacuses are a kind of manual calculating machine which has been used for thousands of years and in some countries is still in use used today as a counting aid for young children. The ancient Greeks, Romans, Etruscans and many other peoples in the Middle East used them, as did the Chinese, Persians and, later on, Europeans.

Abacus is a Latin word derived from the Greek word *abax*, meaning board or table, and that is what they were. They were counting boards or frames with counters, beads or balls which slid up and down in slots or on wires. The boards were usually divided into parallel lines with each section representing a power of 10. Sometimes they were divided yet again into two, so that decimal numbers could be expressed.

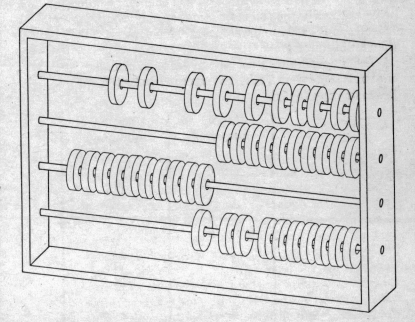

Counting boards were widely used. In Europe they were employed to check calculations which had been done originally with pen and ink, a practice which really didn't die out until the late eighteenth century.

In the first century BC the Chinese used a similar system, but they utilized rods made of bone or ivory, a practice that the Japanese adopted. The use of this type of abacus spread all over the Far East, but today beads are used rather than rods.

Although the use of electronic calculators is widespread today, bead abacuses can be seen in shops and offices all over Japan, China and in many other countries.

Roman numerals

Roman numerals have been in use for a very long time, and even today they are sometimes used as chapter headings in books and can be seen on inscriptions on public buildings. Indeed, many clocks and watches still have roman rather than arabic numerals.

From time to time they were altered and modified. At one point there were 3 different signs in use for 500, before D was finally adopted.

Arabic numerals	Roman numerals
1	I
2	II
3	III
4	IV
5	V
6	VI
7	VII
8	VIII
9	IX
10	X
50	L
100	C
500	D
1000	M

Conversion of roman and arabic numerals

This is not difficult provided you remember that if a larger numeral is in front of a smaller numeral, the smaller is added to the larger, as:

$$XVI = X + V + I$$
$$= 10 + 5 + 1$$
$$= 16$$

$$CLXXVII = 100 + 50 + 10 + 10 + 5 + 1 + 1$$
$$= 177$$

If a smaller numeral is in front of a larger numeral, the smaller must be subtracted from the larger, as:

$$XXIV = X + X + (V - I)$$
$$= 10 + 10 + (5 - 1)$$
$$= 24$$

$$MDCXCII = M + D + C + (C - X) + I + I$$
$$= 1000 + 500 + 100 + (100 - 10) + 1 + 1$$
$$= 1,692$$

Can you write the year in which you were born in roman numerals?

Some early notations

Ancient Egyptian hieroglyphic numerals

Ancient Egyptian hieratic numerals

Hittite hieroglyphic numerals

Assyrian-Babylonian numerals

Early Greek numerals

Cretan hieroglyphic numerals

Numbers 1–10 in some languages

Number	Anglo-Saxon	Breton	Danish	Dutch
1	an	eun	en	een
2	twegen	diou	to	twee
3	þri	tri	tre	drie
4	feower	pevar	fire	vier
5	fif	pemp	fem	vijf
6	six	chouech	seks	zes
7	seofou	seiz	syv	zeven
8	eahta	eiz	otte	acht
9	nigon	nao	ni	negon
10	tyn	dek	ti	tien

English	French	Modern German	Greek	Icelandic
one	un	eins	hén	einn
two	deux	zwei	dúo	tveir
three	trois	drei	treís	prir
four	quatre	vier	téttares	fjorir
five	cinq	fünf	pénte	fimm
six	six	sechs	héx	sex
seven	sept	sieben	heptá	sjö
eight	huit	achte	októ	atta
nine	neuf	neun	ennéa	niu
ten	dix	zehn	déka	tiu

Spanish	Swedish	Sanskrit	Welsh	Arabic
uno	en	éka	un	wahed
dos	twa	dvi	dau	ethnen
tres	tre	tri	tri	thalatha
cuatro	fyra	tchatur	petwar	arbaa
cinco	fem	pañcha	pimp	khamssa
seis	sex	sas	chwe	settah
siete	sju	sapta	seith	sabaa
ocho	atta	asta	wyth	thamania
nueve	nio	nava	naw	tessa
diez	tio	daça	dek	ashara

Number	Irish Gaelic	Italian	Latin	Portuguese	Russian
1	oin	uno	unus	um	odjn
2	da	due	duo	dois	dva
3	tri	tre	tres	tres	tri
4	cethir	quattro	quattuor	quatro	tchetjre
5	coic	cinque	quinque	cinco	pjat'
6	se	sei	sex	seis	chest'
7	secht	sette	septem	sete	sem'
8	ocht	otto	octo	oito	vosem'
9	noi	nove	novem	noue	devjat'
10	deich	dieci	decem	dez	desjat'

Words representing numbers

Many of the following terms are still used, though some are becoming obsolete:

Term	Number
tithe	0·1 ($\frac{1}{10}$)
couple	2
brace	2
pair	2
half a dozen	6
dozen	12
baker's dozen	13
score (also two score, etc.)	20
gross (dozen dozen)	144
once	1 time
twice	2 times as much/many
thrice	3 times as much/many
fourfold	4 times as much/many
fivefold	5 times as much/many
sixfold	6 times as much/many
sevenfold	7 times as much/many
eightfold	8 times as much/many
ninefold	9 times as much/many

Measurement

As soon as man needed to be able to measure things, he found a way of doing so. When he wanted to measure the length of something, he literally used whatever came to hand.

A palm measures about 3 inches. It is the inner part of the surface of a hand between the fingers and the wrist.

A hand measures about 4 inches. That is the distance between the tip of a man's thumb and the tip of the little finger when the fingers are extended.

A cubit measures about 18 inches. It is the distance from the elbow to the end of the middle finger.

The Romans used their feet for measurement, but their foot was a little shorter than ours. They divided its length into 12 and called the smaller measurement *uncia*, meaning twelfth part, which is why we use 'inch' for the twelfth part of our foot.

Of course things got out of hand at times. The people in one country had bigger hands or feet than in another, and every now and again someone tried to do something about it. In England, Edward I had a go. His measure for an inch was 3 grains of barley, 12 inches made a foot and 3 feet made an ulna. This caused some trouble with the Saxons, because Edward I's new foot was longer than the Roman foot but shorter than the Saxon foot. They thought that they would lose out on land measurement, so the King invented a new measurement; this was the rod, $16\frac{1}{2}$ of his new feet, whereas the old Saxon measurement was the equivalent of 15 feet. The rumblings died away. This way the Saxons gained something. For hundreds of years the mile was 4,800 Saxon feet, but in Elizabeth I's reign it was changed to the present-day 5,280 feet (1,760 yards or 1,609 metres).

● It was the French who introduced the metric system which became legal in 1801. They divided the distance from the North Pole to the Equator into 10,000,000 parts. One part became a unit of length and was called a metre, a word derived from the Greek *metron*, which means to measure. The system became legal in the UK in 1897 and was officially adopted in 1971.

2 | MONEY

Any commodity which is a recognised method of exchange is a kind of money. All sorts of things have been used. In many countries cattle were accepted as the universal currency, in others furs, cloth, shells, jade and seashells were the means of exchange.

Early man obtained goods by bartering. An animal, for instance, might have been exchanged for grain, but there were disadvantages to this. Someone might have to accept more grain than he really wanted, so he would have to barter the surplus for something else that he needed.

It soon became apparent that a common means of exchange had to be found and that it must be something which everyone recognised and which was durable – and it should preferably be indestructible. It also had to be portable. Metal was the answer: copper, bronze, gold and silver were used. By the seventh century BC the Lydians were using coins which were of uniform weight and had been officially stamped. Money as we know it had appeared!

The currency of most countries today consists of notes and coins. However, the widespread use of credit cards has introduced a new phrase into our vocabulary – plastic money.

Currency used in ancient and medieval worlds

Although the coins listed below are now obsolete, their names are still familiar to us. In the New Testament, for instance, we are told that a poor widow gave her mite to those even worse off. A mite was worth very little, and in England hundreds of years ago, it was worth a half farthing. Long John's parrot in *Treasure Island* croaked 'Pieces of Eight, Pieces of Eight'. This was an old Spanish dollar which was called a *peso*. Some of the names of coins such as the *drachma* and the *mark* are still used but they no longer refer to gold and silver coins as they did originally.

Coin	Origin
denarius	Roman silver coin, the New Testament penny, its initial letter became the 'd' in pre-decimalisation £ s d; also a Roman gold coin equivalent to 25 silver denarii
doubloon	Spanish or Portuguese gold coin which varied in value but which was twice the value of a pistole; also used in South America
drachma	Greek silver coin; also a unit of weight approximately equivalent in value to the weight of the coin
ducat	gold or silver coins which varied in value, used in a number of European countries
florin	Florentine thirteenth-century gold coin, also gold and silver coins used in other European countries (*see also* Old UK currency)
groat	English silver coin worth fourpence, also used in the Low Countries (Netherlands and elsewhere)
guilder	gold and silver coins used in Austria, Germany and the Netherlands
krone	silver coin used in Denmark, Norway and Austria, a 10 mark gold piece in Germany
libra	Peruvian gold coin, also the pound, a unit of weight, its initial letter became the '£' in the pre-decimalisation £ s d
mark	Scottish silver coin equivalent in value to 13s 4d (66p); German silver coin; also European unit of weight for approximately 8 ounces of gold and silver
mite	coin of very little value used in Middle East; in England worth half a farthing

napoleon	French gold coin equivalent in value to 20 francs with portrait of the Emperors Napoleon I or III on one face
obolus	Greek coin worth 0.166 drachma, also used in Europe
piece of eight	Spanish and South American silver dollar equivalent in value to 8 reals
pistole	Spanish gold coin, also used in other European countries
real	Spanish silver coin
sequin	Venetian gold coin, used elsewhere in Italy
shekel	Hebrew half-ounce gold or silver coin, previously a weight
solidus	Roman gold coin originally called a bezani, its initial letter became the 's' in pre-decimalisation £ s d
talent	a unit of weight of silver or gold coins equivalent to about 26 kg (58 lbs) used in Greece, Rome and the Middle East
taler (thaler)	German silver coin

Old UK currency

On 15 February 1971, the UK changed from its old style money to decimal coinage. Of course, over the centuries there had been many changes in both the value and the type of coins issued. The groat – a silver coin worth fourpence – had disappeared long ago, and the halfpenny – first introduced in the thirteenth century – had become a copper coin instead of a silver one. However, the introduction of decimalisation was a turning point in the history of British coinage.

Name	Value	Slang term
1 farthing	$\frac{1}{4}$ penny	――――
1 halfpenny	2 farthings	――――
1 sixpence	6 pennies	tanner
12 pennies	1 shilling	bob
1 florin	2 shillings	two bob
1 half-crown	$2\frac{1}{2}$ shillings	half-dollar
1 crown	5 shillings	dollar
20 shillings	1 pound	quid, oncer, nicker
21 shillings	1 guinea	――――

Some facts about old UK currency

farthing	: introduced 1279, withdrawn 1960.
halfpenny	: introduced 1280, withdrawn 1969.
penny	: introduced 8th century, demonetized 1971.
threepenny piece	: introduced 1551, demonetized 1971.
shilling	: introduced 16th century, now 5p coin.
florin	: introduced 1849, now 10p coin.
half-crown	: introduced 15th century, withdrawn 1970.

UK currency today

Denomination	Standard weight (g)	Standard diameter (cm)	Metal
1 penny	3.564	2.032	bronze
2 pence	7.128	2.591	bronze
5 pence	5.66518	2.3595	cupro-nickel
10 pence	11.31036	2.85	cupro-nickel
20 pence	5.0	2.14	cupro-nickel
50 pence	13.5	3.0	cupro-nickel
£1 coin	9.5	2.25	cupro-nickel-zinc
£2 coin	15.98	2.84	cupro-nickel-zinc

Bank notes are issued in denominations of £5, £10, £20 and £50.

Legal tender

If someone went into a shop and wanted to pay a bill of £1 with 1 or 2 pence coins, the shopkeeper could refuse to accept the money on the grounds that they are not legal tender.

Denomination and limit of legal tender

Coin	Limit
bronze coins (1p, 2p)	up to 20p
cupro-nickel coins (5p, 10p)	up to £5
cupro-nickel coins (20p, 50p)	up to £10
£1 and £2 coins	up to any amount
notes and gold coins dating from 1838	up to any amount

Gold coins

Britannia gold bullion coins with denominations of £100, £50, £25 and £10 were introduced in October 1987.

● If you happen to be lucky enough to possess gold coins which are more than fifty years old and are worth at least £8,000, you should remember that you cannot export them without getting permission from the Department of Trade and Industry.

Notes in circulation in the UK

The number of notes in circulation goes up every year:

Year	£5 notes	£10 notes	£20 notes	£50 notes
1984	2,544,630,255	4,845,942,570	1,978,602,740	909,237,800
1988	1,896,164,954	5,810,057,500	2,932,344,920	1,755,115,450

Currency in Australia

Denomination (coins)	Value (A$)
1 cent	0.01 ($\frac{1}{100}$)
2 cents	0.02 ($\frac{1}{50}$)
5 cents	0.05 ($\frac{1}{20}$)
10 cents	0.1 ($\frac{1}{10}$)
20 cents	0.2 ($\frac{1}{5}$)
50 cents	0.5 ($\frac{1}{2}$)

Notes are issued in denominations of A$ 1, 2, 5, 10 and 50.

Currency in Canada

Denomination (coins)	Value (C$)
1 cent	0.01 ($\frac{1}{100}$)
5 cents	0.05 ($\frac{1}{20}$)
10 cents	0.1 ($\frac{1}{10}$)
25 cents	0.25 ($\frac{1}{4}$)
50 cents	0.5 ($\frac{1}{2}$)
C$ 1	1.0

Notes are issued in denominations of C$ 1, 2, 5, 10, 20, 50, 100, 500 and 1000.

Currency in the USA

Denomination (coins)	Value ($)	Common name
1 cent	0.01 ($\frac{1}{100}$)	penny
5 cents	0.05 ($\frac{1}{20}$)	nickel
10 cents	0.1 ($\frac{1}{10}$)	dime
25 cents	0.25 ($\frac{1}{4}$)	quarter
50 cents	0.5 ($\frac{1}{2}$)	half dollar

Notes are issued in denominations of $ 1, 2, 5, 10, 20, 50 and 100.

Currency throughout the world

Country	Monetary unit
Afghanistan	1 afghani = 100 puls
Albania	1 lek = 100 qindarka
Algeria	1 dinar = 100 centimes (Algerian dinar)
Andorra	uses Spanish and French currency
Angola	1 quanza = 100 lweis
Antigua, Barbuda	1 dollar = 100 cents (East Caribbean dollar EC$)
Argentina	1 austral = 100 centavos = 1000 pesos
Australia	1 dollar = 100 cents (Australian dollar A$)
Austria	1 schilling = 100 groschen

Bahamas	1 dollar = 100 cents (Bahamian dollar B$)
Bahrain	1 dinar = 1000 fils (Bahrainian dinar)
Bangladesh	1 taka = 100 paisa
Barbados	1 dollar = 100 cents (Barbados dollar B$)
Belgium	1 franc = 100 centimes (Belgium franc)
Belize	1 dollar = 100 cents (Belizean dollar BZ$)
Benin	franc (franc de la Communauté Financière Africaine CFA franc)
Bermuda	1 dollar = 100 francs
Bhutan	1 ngultrum = 100 chetrums (also uses Indian currency)
Bolivia	1 peso = 100 centavos
Botswana	1 pula = 100 thebe
Brazil	1 cruzado = 100 cruzeiros
Brunei	1 dollar = 100 sen (Brunei dollar)
Bulgaria	1 lev = 100 stotinki
Burkino Faso	CFA franc
Burma	1 kyat = 100 pyas
Burundi	1 franc = 100 centimes (Burundi franc)
Cameroon	CFA franc
Canada	1 dollar = 100 cents (Canadian dollar C$)
Cape Verde	1 escudo = 100 centavos (escudo Capoverdianos)
Cayman Islands	1 dollar = 100 cents
Central African Republic	CFA franc
Chad	CFA franc
Chile	1 peso = 100 centavos (Chilean peso)
China (mainland)	1 yuan = 10 jiao or chia = 100 fen
Colombia	1 peso = 100 centavos (Colombian peso)
Comoros	CFA franc

Congo	CFA franc
Costa Rica	1 colón = 100 céntimos
Cuba	1 peso = 100 centavos (Cuban peso)
Cyprus	1 pound = 100 cents (Cyprus pound £C)
Czechoslovakia	1 koruna = 100 haleru
Denmark	1 krone = 100 øre (Danish krone)
Djibouti	1 franc = 100 centimes (Djibouti franc)
Dominica	EC$
Dominican Republic	1 peso = 100 centavos (Dominican Republic peso)
Ecuador	1 sucre = 100 centavos
Egypt	1 pound = 100 piastres (Egyptian pound £E)
El Salvador	1 colón = 100 centavos (Salvadorian colón)
Equatorial Guinea	CFA franc
Ethiopia	1 birr = 100 cents
Falkland Islands	1 pound = 100 pence
Faroe Islands	1 krone = 100 øre
Fiji	1 dollar = 100 cents (Fiji dollar F$)
Finland	1 markka = 100 penniä
France	1 franc = 100 centimes (French franc)
Gabon	CFA franc
Gambia	1 dalasi = 100 butut
Germany, East	1 mark = 100 pfennigs (mark der Deutschen Demokratischen Republik DDR mark)
Germany, West	1 deutsche mark = 100 pfennige (Deutsche mark DM)
Ghana	1 cedi = 100 pesewas
Greece	1 drachma = 100 lepta
Grenada	EC dollar
Guatemala	1 quetzel = 100 centavos
Guinea	1 syli = 100 cauris
Guinea-Bissau	1 pesos = 100 centavos (Guinea peso)

Guyana	1 dollar = 100 cents (Guyanan dollar G$)
Haiti	1 gourde = 100 centimes
Honduras	1 lempira = 100 centavos
Hong Kong	1 dollar = 100 cents
Hungary	1 forint = 100 fillér
Iceland	1 krona = 100 aurar
India	1 rupee = 100 paisa (Indian rupee)
Indonesia	1 rupiah = 100 sen
Iran	1 rial = 100 dinars (Iranian rial)
Iraq	1 dinar = 5 riyals = 20 dirhams = 1000 fils
Irish Republic	1 pound or punt = 100 pence (Irish pound £RE)
Israel	1 shekel = 100 agorot
Italy	1 lira = 100 centesimi
Ivory Coast	CFA franc
Jamaica	1 dollar = 100 cents (Jamaican dollar J$)
Japan	1 yen = 100 sen
Jordan	1 dinar = 1000 fils (Jordanian dinar)
Kampuchea	1 riel = 100 sen
Kenya	1 shilling = 100 cents (20 shillings = 1 Kenyan pound £K)
Kiribati	uses Australian currency
Korea, North	1 won = 100 chon or jun
Korea, South	1 won = 100 chon or jeon
Kuwait	1 dinar = 1000 fils (Kuwaiti dinar)
Laos	1 kip = 100 at
Lebanon	1 pound = 100 piastres (Lebanese pound £L)
Lesotho	1 loti = 100 lisente
Liberia	1 dollar = 100 cents (Liberian dollar L$)

Libya	1 dinar = 1000 dirhams (Libyan dinar)
Liechtenstein	uses Swiss currency
Luxemburg	1 franc = 100 centimes (Luxemburg franc)
Macau	1 pataca = 100 avos
Madagascar	1 franc = 100 centimes (Malagasy franc)
Malawi	1 kwacha = 100 tambala
Malaysia	1 ringgit (Malaysian dollar) = 100 sen
Maldive Islands	1 rufiyaa (Maldavian rupee) = 100 sen
Mali	CFA franc (1 CFA franc = 2 Mali francs)
Malta	1 lira or pound = 100 cents (Maltese £ML)
Mauritania	1 ouguiya = 5 khoums
Mauritius	1 rupee = 100 cents (Mauritian rupee)
Mexico	1 peso = 100 centavos (Mexican peso)
Monaco	uses French currency
Mongolia	1 tugrik = 100 möngö
Morocco	1 dirham = 100 centimes
Mozambique	1 metical = 100 centavos
Nauru	uses Australian currency
Nepal	1 rupee = 100 paisa (Nepalese rupee)
Netherlands	1 guilder or florin = 100 cents
New Zealand	1 dollar = 100 cents (New Zealand dollar NZ$)
Nicaragua	1 córdoba = 100 centavos
Niger	CFA franc
Nigeria	1 naira = 100 kobo
Norway	1 krone = 100 øre (Norwegian krone)
Oman	1 rial = 1000 baiza (Omani rial)
Pakistan	1 rupee = 100 paisa (Pakistani rupee)
Panama	1 balboa = 100 centesimos
Papua New Guinea	1 kina = 100 toea
Paraguay	1 guarani = 100 céntimos

Peru	1 inti = 100 céntimos
Philippines	1 peso = 100 céntavos (Philippines peso)
Poland	1 złoty = 100 groszy
Portugal	1 escudo = 100 centavos
Qatar	1 riyal = 100 dirhams (Qatar riyal)
Romania	1 leu = 100 bani
Rwanda	1 franc = 100 centimes (Rwandan franc)
St Helena	1 pound = 100 pence
St Lucia	EC dollar
St Vincent and Grenadines	EC dollar
San Marino	uses Italian currency
São Tomé and Principé	1 dobra = 100 centimos
Saudi Arabia	1 riyal = 20 qursh = 100 halalah
Senegal	CFA franc
Seychelles	1 rupee = 100 cents (Seychelles rupee)
Sierra Leone	1 leone = 100 cents
Singapore	1 dollar = 100 cents (Singapore dollar $S)
Solomon Islands	1 dollar = 100 cents (Solomon dollar $SI)
Somalia	1 shilling = 100 centesimi
South Africa	1 rand = 100 cents
Spain	1 peseta = 100 céntimos
Sri Lanka	1 rupee = 100 cents (Sri Lankan rupee)
Sudan	1 pound = 100 piastres (Sudanese pound £S)
Suriname	1 guilder = 100 cents (Suriname guilder)
Swaziland	1 lilangeni = 100 cents
Sweden	1 krona = 100 øre
Switzerland	1 franc = 100 centimes or rappen (Swiss franc)

Syria	1 pound = 100 piastres (Syrian pound £S)
Taiwan	1 dollar = 100 cents
Tanzania	1 shilling = 100 cents
Thailand	1 baht = 100 satangs
Togo	CFA franc
Tonga	1 pa'anga = 100 seniti
Trinidad and Tobago	1 dollar = 100 cents (Trinidad and Tobago dollar $TT)
Tunisia	1 dinar = 100 millimes (Tunisian dinar)
Turkey	1 lira = 100 kurus
Turks and Caicos Islands	uses USA dollars
Tuvalu	uses Australian currency
Uganda	1 shilling = 100 cents (Ugandan shilling)
United Arab Emirates	1 dirham = 100 fils (United Arab Emirates dirham)
UK	1 pound = 100 pence
USA	1 dollar = 100 cents (US$)
USSR	1 rouble = 100 kopeks
Upper Volta	CFA franc
Uruguay	1 peso = 100 centésimos
Vanatu	vatu
Vatican City	uses Italian currency
Venezuela	1 bolivar = 100 centimos
Virgin Islands	uses USA dollars
Western Samoa	1 tala = 100 sene
Yemen Arab Republic	1 riyal = 100 fils (Yemeni riyal)
Yemen, People's Democratic Republic	1 dinar = 1000 fils (Yemeni PDR dinar)
Yugoslavia	1 dinar = 100 paras

Zaire	1 zaire = 100 makuta = 10,000 senahi
Zambia	1 kwacha = 100 ngwee
Zimbabwe	1 dollar = 100 cents (Z$)

Corinthian 6th C. BC

Israel 1973

US Shilling 1667

Delhi Rupee 1300

China 1831

Denarius 68-66 BC

3 | TIME

The life of primitive people was ruled by the sun. When it became light, they got up. When it became dark they went to bed but as they developed they devised methods of measuring time, although it varied from one group of people to another.

Early Egyptians established a 10-day week, the Assyrians had a 6-day week and then, about 6,000 years ago, the Babylonians decided that a week should be 7 days long and that, since the 4 phases of the moon each lasted for 7 days, a month should consist of 4 weeks. Gradually, other races adopted this system.

It was the Egyptians who divided the day into hours. They did it simply by using an upright stick and noting the length and position of its shadow rather like a sundial. Later, they devised a water clock. The measurement of time was now well under way.

The time table

60 thirds	= 1 second
60 seconds	= 1 minute
60 minutes	= 1 hour
24 hours	= 1 day
7 days	= 1 week
52 weeks	= 1 year = 12 calendar months
	= 13 lunar months
1 year	= 365 days
1 leap year	= 366 days
10 years	= 1 decade
10 decades	= 1 century
10 centuries	= 1 millenium

The calendar

The calendar is a way of marking the beginning, divisions and length of a year.

● A calendar day is 24 hours long. It begins at midnight and is divided into 24 hours of 60 minutes each, and each minute into 60 seconds. Unless the 24-hour clock is used,

the morning – am (ante meridian) – begins at midnight
and ends at noon. Afternoon – pm (post meridian) – begins
after noon and ends at midnight, but there are other
divisions. Morning can be considered the early part of the
morning to noon; afternoon from after midday to evening,
evening roughly 18.00 to midnight, and night from late
evening to dawn.

● The week lasts for 7 days, but its beginning and end
varies from place to place. In Christian countries the week
runs from Sunday to Saturday, although the working week
begins on Monday. In China, for instance, the week runs
from Monday to Sunday and in many East African
countries from Friday to Thursday.

The origin of the Gregorian calendar

Many countries all over the world use the Gregorian
calendar. Even those which have a different calendar
system recognize it and often use it in conjunction with
their own.

Previously the Julian calendar was used. This was
introduced by Julius Caesar in 45 BC. Because of an
inaccuracy, however, by the late sixteenth century there
was a difference of 11 days between the calendar and the
equinoctial year – the time it takes for the earth to revolve
around the sun.

Pope Gregory XIII decided that this had to be put right,
so in 1582 he ordained that in that year 5 October should
be called 15 October. The Catholic countries of France,
Italy, Portugal and Spain immediately conformed, and in
the following year many other countries followed suit. The
acceptance of the new calendar continued to spread and by
1600 Scotland was using it. However, it wasn't until 1752
that Parliament decided it was time to fall into line and
decreed that England, Ireland, Wales and the British
colonies should also adopt it.

There were howls of protest and crowds paraded round
the streets yelling 'Give us back our eleven days.' The
ignorant – and especially those whose birthdays fell on the
missing days – felt that somehow a piece of their lives was

being lopped off. But it made no difference. Parliament stood firm and although they rumbled and mumbled, the population accepted the Gregorian calendar. At last Britain was in step with the rest of the world.

Calendar years

- A calendar year is made up of 365 days, but this is inaccurate since an average solar year is slightly longer.
- A solar year is also called an astronomical year, an equinoctial or a tropical year, and consists of 365.24219878 average solar days.
- In the Gregorian calendar, leap years compensate for the extra .24219878 of a solar day. An extra day is added on to the end of February every fourth year (with the exception of centennial years, e.g. 1900), unless the number of the century itself is exactly divisible by 4. This means that the year AD 2000 will be a leap year.

Leap years in the twentieth century

1904	1924	1944	1964	1984
1908	1928	1948	1968	1988
1912	1932	1952	1972	1992
1916	1936	1956	1976	1996
1920	1940	1960	1980	2000

Months of the year

There are 12 months in the year. The origin of their names stems from the old Roman calendar, which started in March.

Month	Origin	Length
January	from the Latin *Januarius* after Janus, the Roman god of beginnings, who had two faces and looked both backwards and forwards.	31 days
February	from the Latin *Februarius*, which means to purify or cleanse when the Romans prepared to welcome their new year.	28 or 29
March	from the Latin *Martius* named after Mars the Roman god of war, but also associated with growth and vegetation.	31
April	from the Latin *aperire*, to open as buds do, or from the Latin *Aprilis* – the month devoted to Venus, the goddess of love.	30
May	from the Latin *Maius*, the Greek goddess concerned with increase; but perhaps from Maiores, the elders.	31
June	probably for the goddess Juno, a month for the young and favoured.	30
July	from the Latin *Iulius* after the Emperor Julius Caesar, named in his honour following his assassination in 44 BC; previously called Quintilis, the 5th month.	31

August	from the Emperor Augustus, named in his honour after his death; previously called Sextilis, the 6th month.	31
September	from Latin *septem*, seven, and *imber*, a shower of rain, the 7th month.	30
October	from Latin *octo*, eight, the 8th month.	31
November	from Latin *novem*, nine, the 9th month.	30
December	from Latin *decem*, ten, the 10th month.	31

Calendar and lunar months

Calendar months are any of the 12 divisions of a year.
● Lunar months are the periods between one new moon and the next. They are 29 days, 12 hours, 44 minutes and approximately 2.7 seconds long.
● Perhaps the various lengths of the months of the year are easier to recall if one has learned the nursery rhyme:

> *30 days hath September*
> *April, June and November,*
> *All the rest have 31 except for February alone*
> *Which has 28 days clear*
> *And 29 in each leap year*

The Islamic calendar

The Hegira is the day on which the Prophet Muhammad left the city of Mecca for that of Medina. The year in which this occurred corresponds to AD 622.
● Hegira years are used in very many Middle Eastern countries, in Turkey and in parts of India, Pakistan, Malaysia and elsewhere. They are lunar years with alternate months 29 or 30 days long. An extra day is added to the end of the year at stated intervals in 30-year cycles.

This means that the Hegira year is 11 or 12 days shorter than years reckoned in the Gregorian calendar, so although the calendar started later the years are gradually getting closer to each other.

Islamic calendar	Gregorian calendar
1410 AH	3 August 1989
1411 AH	23 July 1990
1412 AH	12 July 1991
1413 AH	1 July 1992
1414 AH	20 June 1993
1415 AH	9 June 1994
1416 AH	30 May 1995
1417 AH	18 May 1996
1418 AH	8 May 1997
1419 AH	27 April 1998
1420 AH	16 April 1999

Note: AH = After Hegira

Months of the year

Name	Length
Muharram	30
Safar	29
Rabia I	30
Rabia II	29
Jumada I	30
Jumada II	29
Rajab	30
Shaban	29
Ramadan	30
Shawwai	29
Zu'lkadah	30
Zu'lhijjah	29 or 30 in leap years

The Jewish calendar

The Jewish calendar dates from the creation of the world,
i.e. 1 Tishri 3760 BC, with the letters AM or Year of the
World appearing after the number of the year.
● This calendar is a combination of the solar and the lunar
year like many others, including the Islamic calendar.
● There are 12 lunar months which are 29 or 30 days long.
To make up for the difference between the solar and the
lunar year, an extra month is included 7 times in a cycle of
19 years. These occur on the 3rd, 6th, 8th, 11th, 14th, 17th
and 19th years in each cycle. This extra month comes
towards the end of March or early in April.

Conversion of Jewish and Gregorian calendars

To convert the Jewish year to the Gregorian year, add 1240
to the number of the Jewish year, as:

710 AM + 1240 = AD 1950

To convert the Gregorian year to the Jewish year, ignore
the thousands in the number of years and subtract 240, as:

AD 1950 = 950 − 240 = 710 AM

The Chinese calendar

Until 1911 the Chinese used a lunar calendar, but then
they adopted the Gregorian calendar. Although the lunar
calendar is officially banned, it is probably still in use in
some of the remoter parts of China as well as in areas of
south-eastern China.
● Where the calendar is still used, it consists of a lunar
calendar with 12 months of 29 or 30 days. A 13th month is
included every 3rd or 4th year to bring it into line with the
solar calendar.
● The New Year begins on the 1st day of the 1st lunar
month, so it can fall as early as 21 January or as late as
19 February.
● The calendar has a cycle of 12 years, each symbolised by
a creature. The story is that a Chinese emperor decided to
give a New Year's party. Being a kindly man, he sent an
invitation to a representative of each creature on earth.
When the great day arrived, he was very hurt when only

12 of them turned up. To show his approval of those who came and his great displeasure with those who had not, he created the 12-year cycle naming the years after the creatures who had turned up in order of their arrival.

Chinese Year	Symbol	Chinese Year	Symbol
1972	rat	1978	horse
1973	ox	1979	goat
1974	tiger	1980	monkey
1975	hare	1981	rooster
1976	dragon	1982	dog
1977	snake	1983	pig
		1984	rat
		1985	ox
		1986	tiger
		1987	hare
		1988	dragon
		1989	snake
		1990	horse
		1991	goat

The Russian calendar

The Gregorian calendar is in use in the USSR, but their method of designating which year is a leap year is a more accurate way of doing so than in the west. If the number of the year is divided by 9 and the remainder is either 2 or 6, then that year will be a leap year, e.g:

1995 ÷ 9 = 221, remainder 6
1995 will be a leap year in the USSR
2001 ÷ 9 = 222, remainder 3
2001 will not be a leap year in the USSR

This system means that the Russian calendar will not have to be adjusted by a day for another 45,000 years, but in the west the calendar will have to be adjusted by one day in about 4,000 years.

The Japanese calendar

The Japanese use the Gregorian calendar with the same length of weeks and months, but the numbers of the years are based on epochs or periods which in general start at the beginning of the reign of an emperor. When Emperor Akihito ascended the throne in Japan in 1989, the number of years began from that event.

Words used for periods of time

The words listed below all relate to a period of time. Biannual, for instance, means twice a year, so it is something that happens every sixth month. A tercentenary is a period of 300 years, or is the 300th celebration or anniversary of an event.
● Not every year has a special name. Often they are described by the word decade meaning 10 years, so 40 years is described as the fourth decade.

Word	Period of time
quarter	3 months
biannual	6 months
annual	1 year
biennial	2 years
triennial	3 years
quadrennial	4 years
quinquennial	5 years
sextennial	6 years

septennial	7 years
octennial	8 years
decade	10 years
quindecennial	15 years
century	100 years
bicentenary	200 years
tercentenary	300 years
quadricentenary	400 years
millenium	10 centuries
aeon	immeasurably long time
aeon (geologically)	1,000 million years
epoch	the beginning of a new and important period in history acting as a marker for succeeding years
epoch (geologically)	a subdivision of a geological period made up of a number of ages, e.g. Pleistocene; several epochs form a period
from time immemorial	strictly speaking any period of time up to 1189, now used to indicate time so long ago as to be vague

Working out days of the week from 1800 to 1999

It is possible to work out on which day of the week any date of the year fell or falls from 1800 to 1999. Most people want to know the day of the week on which they were born since:

> *Monday's child is fair of face,*
> *Tuesday's child is full of grace,*
> *Wednesday's child is full of woe,*
> *Thursday's child has far to go,*
> *Friday's child is loving and giving,*
> *Saturday's child works hard for its living,*
> *But the child that is born on the Sabbath Day*
> *Is bonny and blithe and good and gay.*

You can actually work out these days in your head if you memorize the list given below for the values of the days of the week and months of the year.

1800–1899				1900–1999	
Day	**Value**	**Month**	**Value**	**Day**	**Value**
Monday	6	January	0	Monday	1
Tuesday	0	February	3	Tuesday	2
Wednesday	1	March	3	Wednesday	3
Thursday	2	April	6	Thursday	4
Friday	3	May	1	Friday	5
Saturday	4	June	4	Saturday	6
Sunday	5	July	6	Sunday	0
		August	2		
		September	5		
		October	0		
		November	3		
		December	5		

The method of working out the day of the week is simple:

For 1 October 1946:

(a) **Add together:**

   1)   the date itself   1   = 1 +

   2)   the value of the month   October = 0

   3)   the year of the century   1946 = 46

   4)   the number of leap years
in the century (divide last
2 digits by 4), ignore
remainder   46 ÷ 4   = 11

                                                58

(b)   Divide total by 7   58 ÷ 7   = 8 remainder 2

(c)   The remainder is the answer
remainder = 2 = Tuesday in the table of
values 1900–1999

1 October 1946 fell on a Tuesday.

For 18 August 1937:

(a)   Add together:
  1)   the date   = 18 +
  2)   the value of the month   = 2
  3)   the years of the century   = 37
  4)   the number of leap years = 9

                                       66

(b) $66 \div 7$ = 9 remainder 3
(c)   remainder = 3 = Wednesday in the table of
      values 1900–1999

18 August 1937 fell on a Wednesday.

For 30 November 1874:

(a) $30 + 3 + 74 + 18$ = 125
(b) $125 \div 7$ = 17 remainder 6
(c)   remainder = 6 (Monday in the 1800–1899 table)

30 November 1874 fell on a Monday.

For 12 May 1990:

(a) $12 + 1 + 90 + 22$ = 125
(b) $125 \div 7$ = 17 remainder 6
(c)   remainder = 6 Saturday in the 1900–1999 table

12 May 1990 fell on a Saturday.

It is possible to speed up the method of finding the day on which a date will fall by dividing each individual number by 7 and adding together only the remainders. The sum of the remainders is then itself divided by 7. As before, looking up the final remainder in the table of values will give you the answer:

For 22 August 1926:

Usual method:

$$22 + 2 + 26 + 6 = 56 \div 7 = 8 \text{ remainder } 0 = \text{Sunday}$$

Using remainders only:

$$1 + 2 + 5 + 6 = 14 \div 7 = 2 \text{ remainder } 0 = \text{Sunday}$$

For 25 December 1992:

Usual method:

$$25 + 5 + 92 + 23 = 145 \div 7 = 20 \text{ remainder } 5 = \text{Friday}$$

Using remainders only:

$$4 + 5 + 1 + 2 = 12 \div 7 = 1 \text{ remainder } 5 = \text{Friday}$$

Quarter days and Scottish Term days

These are the 4 days of the year on which rent should be paid and the settlement of debts, payment of interest and other financial settlements should be made.

● In England, Northern Ireland and Wales these are called Quarter Days, and they have been adopted in many other countries. In Scotland they are known as Term Days. All of them are connected with the Church calendar.

Quarter Days	Date	Religious significance
Lady Day	25 March	Feast of the Annunciation.
Midsummer Day	24 June	Feast of St John the Baptist.
Michaelmas Day	29 September	Feast of St Michael and All Angels.
Christmas Day	25 December	Feast of the Nativity.

Term Days	Date	Religious significance
Candlemas	2 February	Feast of the Purification.
Whit Sunday		Pentecost. Whit Sunday is 7 weeks after Easter Sunday.
Lammas	1 August	A kind of harvest festival; bread baked from the first crop of wheat was consecrated at Loaf Mass on that day.
Martinmas	11 November	St Martin's Day.

The tax year

The reason why the tax year in the UK begins on 5 April goes back to the changeover from the Julian to the Gregorian calendar. The tax year had traditionally started on the day following Lady Day, one of the quarter days (see above). Although the calendar moved on 11 days, the Church continued to celebrate Lady Day on the old date of 25 March. In spite of that, Parliament decided that since the calendar had marched on 11 days the tax year must march along with it and so, leaving Lady Day behind, it adopted the new date of 5 April.

Canonical hours

Canonical hours are 7 periods of the day assigned to prayer and worship. In convents and monasteries, one person is given the important duty of ringing the bell so that whatever they may be doing, all nuns and monks are called to join in prayer in the chapel. Today, matins and lauds are usually recited together; this should take place at midnight but is often celebrated at daybreak instead.

Canonical hour	Time
matins (with lauds)	12.00 (midnight)
lauds	3.00
prime	6.00
tierce	9.00
sext	12.00 (midday)
nones	15.00 (sometimes earlier)
vespers	18.00
compline	21.00

The Church calendar

Apart from its religious significance, Easter is very important in the Church calendar since the dates on which movable feasts occur are determined by the date of Easter itself.

- **Easter Sunday** is the first Sunday after the full moon occurring on or after the day following 21 March. It can fall on any of the 35 days from 22 March to 25 April.
- **Ash Wednesday** marks the beginning of Lent, the period leading up to Easter. It can fall on any of the days from 4 February to 10 March.
- **Palm Sunday** comes 40 days after Ash Wednesday and marks the beginning of Holy Week.
- **Ascension Day** comes 40 days after Easter Sunday. It can fall from 30 April to 3 June.
- **Rogation Sunday** is the Sunday preceding Ascension Day.
- **Rogation Days** are the Monday, Tuesday and Wednesday following Ascension Day. At one time they were marked by religious processions; now they are the days on which the ceremony of beating the bounds is still carried out in some parishes.
- **Whit Sunday** is 7 weeks after Easter Sunday. It can fall from 10 May to 13 June.
- **Trinity Sunday** is the Sunday following Whit Sunday. Subsequent Sundays are numbered in the Church calendar from 1 as 'after Pentecost'.
- **Corpus Christi** falls on the Thursday after Trinity Sunday.
- **Advent Sunday** is the Sunday closest to St Andrew's Day, 30 November, so that there can be 4 Sundays between Advent Sunday and Christmas Day.
- **Maundy Thursday** precedes Good Friday and is the day on which the Queen distributes maundy money to worthy elderly people.
- **Good Friday** is the Friday preceding Easter Sunday.

Movable feasts 1989–2000

Year	Ash Wednesday	Easter Sunday	Ascension Day	Whit Sunday	Advent
1989	8 February	26 March	4 May	14 May	3 December
1990	28 February	15 April	24 May	3 June	2 December
1991	13 February	31 March	9 May	19 May	1 December
1992	4 March	19 April	28 May	7 June	29 November
1993	24 February	11 April	20 May	30 May	28 November
1994	16 February	3 April	12 May	22 May	27 November
1995	1 March	16 April	25 May	4 June	3 December
1996	21 February	7 April	16 May	26 May	1 December
1997	12 February	30 March	8 May	18 May	30 November
1998	25 February	12 April	21 May	31 May	29 November
1999	17 February	4 April	13 May	23 May	28 November
2000	8 March	23 April	1 June	11 June	3 December

Saint's days and Red Letter days

Although there are over 70 saints mentioned in the Calendar of the Book of Common Prayer, not all of them have special services. This was decided in AD 325 at the Council of Nicaea. As a result only those who are mentioned in the Bible – and All Saints' Day, held on 1 November – have services printed for them in the Book of Common Prayer.

● These days were picked out in early Church calendars by being printed in red ink; therefore they were the original Red Letter days. Nowadays the term is used for any particularly happy day or celebration.

Even today the judges of the Queen's Bench Division at the sittings of criminal courts wear scarlet robes on all Red Letter days and on State occasions.

Dates of Red Letter days

Date	Event
25 January	Conversion of St Paul
2 February	Purification
25 March	St Mark's Day
1 May	St Philip and St John's Day
14 May	St Matthias' Day
11 June	St Barnabas' Day
24 June	St John the Baptist's Day
29 June	St Peter's Day
3 July	St Thomas's Day
25 July	St James's Day
18 October	St Luke's Day
28 October	St Simon and St Jude's Day
1 November	All Saints' Day
30 November	St Andrew's Day

Watches at sea

Daily hours	Name
midnight–04.00	middle watch
04.00–08.00	morning watch
08.00–12.00	forenoon watch
12.00–16.00	afternoon watch
16.00–18.00	1st dog watch
18.00–20.00	last dog watch (Merchant Navy, 2nd dog watch)
20.00–midnight	1st watch

Note: During watches time is marked by bells, each stroke representing every 30 minutes which has passed. This means that at the end of dog watches the bell is struck 4 times. All other watches end with 8 bells. The beginning of the New Year is marked at sea by the striking of 16 bells.

Seasons in the northern hemisphere

The dates when the seasons of the year begin and end are based on the spring (or vernal) and the autumnal equinox, and the winter and summer solstice. There can be very slight variations in dates in some years.

- An equinox occurs when the day and night are approximately equal in length throughout the world, i.e. when the sun is directly overhead at the Equator.
- A solstice occurs in summer and winter when the overhead midday sun is at its maximum or minimum angular distance from the Equator. The longest day is when the sun is vertically overhead at the Tropic of Cancer. The shortest day is when the sun is vertically overhead at the Tropic of Capricorn.

Dates of equinox and solstices

Spring equinox: 21 March
Autumnal equinox: 22 September
Summer solstice: 21 June
Winter solstice: 22 December

Dates of seasons

Spring: 21 March–21 June
Summer: 21 June–23 September
Autumn: 23 September–22 December
Winter: 22 December–21 March

Note: in the southern hemisphere spring and autumn are reversed, as are winter and summer.

International Date Line

This is an internationally agreed time-change line drawn approximately along the meridian, which zig-zags to avoid land in the Pacific Ocean. A crossing of the Date Line means repeating one day when travelling eastwards and losing one day when travelling westwards.

Greenwich Mean Time (GMT) and Standard Time

Greenwich, near London is located on the 0° meridian. It is from GMT that standard time elsewhere in the world is calculated. Remember that there can be variations as some countries have daylight saving hours.

Area	Standard Time (difference in hours from GMT)
Afghanistan	+4.5
Albania	+1
Aleutian Islands	−11
Andaman Islands	+6.5
Angola	+1
Antigua	−4
Argentina	−4
Australia	
Victoria, Queensland, New South Wales, Tasmania	+10
Northern Territory, South Australia	+9.5
Western Australia	+8
Austria	+1
Azores	−2
Bahamas	−5
Bahrain	+3
Bangladesh	+6
Barbados	−4
Bermuda	−4
Bolivia	−4
Botswana	+2
Brazil	
East	−3
West	−4
Brunei	+8
Bulgaria	+2
Burma	+6.5
Canada	
Atlantic Zone	−4
Eastern Zone	−5
Central Zone	−6
Mountain Zone	−7
Pacific Zone	−8
Yukon Territory	−9
Cape Verde Islands	−2
Central African Republic	+1
Chile	−4
China	
Chungking, Lanchow	+7
Peking, Shanghai	+8
Christmas Island	+7
Cook Islands	−10.5
Costa Rica	−6
Cuba	−5
Cyprus	+2
Czechoslovakia	+1
Denmark	+1
Dominican Republic	−5
Ecuador	−5
Egypt	+2
Ethiopia	+3
Falkland Islands	−4
Fiji	+12
Finland	+2
France	+1
Germany	+1
Gibraltar	+1
Greece	+2
Grenada	−4
Guinea	−1
Guyana	−3.75
Haiti	−5
Holland	+1
Honduras	−6
Hong Kong	+8
Hungary	+1
India	+5.5
Indonesia	
Western Zone	+7
Central Zone	+8
Eastern Zone	+9
Iran	+3.5

Iraq	+3	Panama	−5
Ireland	−1	Papua New Guinea	+10
Israel	+2	Paraguay	−4
Italy	+1	Peru	−5
		Philippine Islands	+8
Jamaica	−5	Poland	+1
Japan	+9	Portugal	+1
Jordan	+2	Puerto Rico	−4
Kalaadlit		Romania	+2
Scoresby Sound	−2		
West coast (not		Salvador	−6
Thule)	−3	Santa Cruz Islands	+11
Thule	−4	Saudi Arabia	+3
Kenya	+3	Senegal	−1
Korea		Seychelles	+4
North Korea	+9	Singapore	+7.75
Republic of Korea	+9	Solomon Islands	+11
Kuwait	+3	South Africa	+2
		Spain	+1
Lebanon	+2	Sri Lanka	+5.5
Leeward Islands	−4	Sudan	+2
Libya	+1	Sweden	+1
Luxemburg	+1	Switzerland	+1
		Syria	+2
Madeira	−1		
Malawi	+2	Tahiti	−10
Malaysia		Taiwan	+8
West Malaysia	+7.5	Tanzania	+3
East Malaysia	+8	Thailand	+7
Maldive Islands	+5	Trinidad and Tobago	−4
Malta	+1	Tunisia	+1
Mauritius	+4	Turkey	+2
Mexico	−7		
Mozambique	+2	Uganda	+3
		Uruguay	−3.5
Nepal	+5.5	USA	
New Guinea	+10	Eastern Zone	−5
New Zealand	+12	Central Zone	−6
Nicaragua	−5.75	Mountain Zone	−7
Norway	+1	Pacific Zone	−8
		Alaska	−8
Pakistan	+5	Hawaiian Islands	−10

USSR	
Latvia	+2
Kiev, Leningrad, Moscow, Odessa	+3
Archangel	+4
Omsk	+6
Vladivostok	+10
Venezuela	−4.5
Vietnam	
North	+7
South	+8
Virgin Islands	−4
Windward Islands	−4
Yemen	+3
Yugoslavia	+1
Zambia	+2
Zaire	
Kinshasha	+1
Katanga, Kasai, Kivu	+2
Zimbabwe	+2

- - - - - - - - International
Date Line

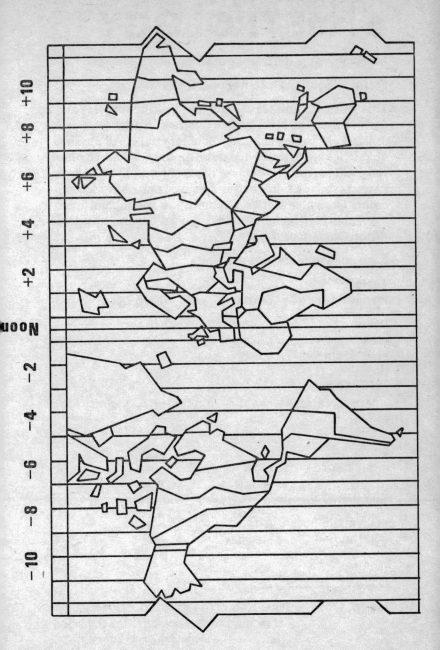

4 | METROLOGY

Metrology is the the science of weight and measures

SI Units (Système International D'Unités)

This system of units is used for all scientific purposes and is derived from the MKS system (metre/kilogram/second). It consists of 7 base and 2 supplementary units. All physical quantities are expressed in these units or in derived units consisting of combinations of these units. Both units have agreed symbols. Some of these derived units have special names (*see* Table 2). Decimal multiples and submultiples (*see* Table 3) in both base and derived units are expressed using standard prefixes.

Base and supplementary SI units

Table 1:

Physical Quantity	SI Unit	Symbol
length	metre	m
mass	kilogram	kg
electric current	ampere	A
time	second	s
thermodynamic temperature	kelvin	K
luminous intensity	candela	cd
amount of substance	mole	mol

Supplementary units

plain angle	radian	rad
solid angle	steradian	sr

Definitions of SI units

metre: length equal to 1,650, 763.73 wavelengths in vacuum corresponding to the transition between the levels $2p_{10}$ and $5d_5$ i.e.

orange to red in the spectrum of the isotope $^{86}_{35}$kr (krypton-86 atom).

kilogram: mass of the international prototype – a cylinder of platinum-iridium in the custody of the Bureau Internationale des Poids et Mésures; equal to 1,000 grams (2.20462 lbs.).

ampere: the intensity of a constant current that if maintained in two straight parallel conductors of infinite length, of negligible circular section and placed at a distance of 1 metre from each other in vacuum, will produce between the conductors a force = 2×10^{-7} newton per metre of length.

second: the time taken by 9,192,631,770 wavelengths of light (as given out by the atom of the radioactive substance, cesium −133) to pass a fixed point.

kelvin unit of thermodynamic temperature: 1/273.16 of the thermodynamic temperature of the triple point of water, i.e. the point at which water, water vapour and ice are in equilibrium.

candela unit of luminous intensity: the luminous intensity, in the perpendicular direction, of a surface of $1/600,000m^2$ of a black body at the temperature of freezing platinum under a pressure of 101,325 pascals.

mole unit of amount of substance: amount of substance of a system containing as many elementary entities as there are atoms in 0.012 kg of carbon-12.

radian plane angle: the plane angle between 2 radii of a circle which cut off an arc on the circumference equal in length to the radius.

steradian unit of solid angle (3-D): the solid angle enclosed at the centre of a sphere by an area at the surface equal to $\frac{\pi}{4}$ of the total area of the sphere, of 1 unit radius.

Derived units are units that are defined in terms of base units. Each has a symbol.

Derived SI units with special names

Quantity	Unit	Symbol
area	square metre	m^2
volume	cubic metre	m^3
acceleration	metre/second squared	$m \cdot s^{-2}$
velocity	metre/second	$m \cdot s^{-1}$
angular velocity	radian/second	$rad \cdot s^{-1}$
angular acceleration	radian/second squared	$rad \cdot s^{-2}$
density	kilogram/cubic metre	$kg \cdot m^{-3}$
frequency	hertz	Hz
momentum	kilogram/metre per second	$kg.m.s^{-1}$
force	newton	n
pressure, stress	pascal	Pa
work, energy, quantity of heat	joule	J
power	watt	W
surface tension	newton/metre	$n \cdot m^{-1}$
temperature	degrees Celsius	°C
heat capacity	joule/kelvin	$J \cdot K^{-1}$
electric charge	coulomb	C
electric resistance	ohm	Ω
electromotive force, potential difference	volt	V
electric conductance	siemens	S
electric capacitance	farad	F
inductance	henry	H
magnetic flux density (magnetic induction)	tesla	T
magnetomotive force	ampere	A
luminous flux	lumen	lm
illumination (illuminance)	lux	lx
radiation activity	becquerel	Bq

Decimal multiples and submultiples used with SI units and definitions

Submultiple	Prefix	Symbol	Multiple	Prefix	Symbol
10^{-1}	deci	d	10^{1}	deca	da
10^{-2}	centi	c	10^{2}	hecto	h
10^{-3}	milli	m	10^{3}	kilo	k
10^{-6}	micro	μ	10^{6}	mega	M
10^{-9}	nano	n	10^{9}	giga	G
10^{-12}	pico	p	10^{10}	tera	T
10^{-15}	femto	f			
10^{-18}	atto	a			

Definitions of SI units with special names

metre: see above

second: see above

radian: the angle subtended at the centre of a circle by an arc equal in length to the radius of the circle, 2π radian = 360°, 1 radian = 57.296°.

kilogram: see above.

hertz: the frequency (e.g. of wavelength) of a periodic phenomenon with a periodic time of 1 second, equal to 1 cycle per second.

newton: force needed to give a mass of 1 kilogram an acceleration of 1 metre per second per second.

pascal: unit of pressure equal to 1 newton per square metre.

joule: the work done when the point of application of the force of 1 newton is displaced through a distance of 1 metre in the direction of the force.

watt: the energy expended per second by a constant electric current of 1 ampere flowing through a conductor with ends maintained at a potential difference of 1 volt; equal to 1 joule per second.

kelvin: see above.

coulomb: the quantity of electricity transferred in a conductor by 1 ampere in 1 second.

ohm: the resistance between 2 points of a conductor when a constant difference of potential of 1 volt applied between the points produces a current of 1 ampere in the conductor.

volt: the difference of a potential between 2 points on a conducting wire carrying a constant current of 1 ampere when the power dissipated between the points equals 1 watt.

siemens: conductance of an element or circuit with a resistance of 1 ohm.

farad: a unit of capacitance in a capacitor (condenser) when, between two plates (separated by a gap) and charged with 1 coulomb of electricity, a potential difference of 1 volt is measured.

henry: a unit of inductance in a closed circuit when a rate of charge of current of 1 ampere/second produces an induced electromotive force (EMF) of 1 volt.

Metric and Imperial Systems

Prefixes and values used in the metric system

Prefix	UK Value	Factor	Symbol
atto	1 trillionth 1 quintillionth (USA)	$\times 10^{-18}$	a
femto	1 thousand billionth 1 quadrillionth (USA)	$\times 10^{-15}$	f
pico	1 billionth 1 trillionth (USA)	$\times 10^{-12}$	p
nano	1 thousand millionth 1 billionth (USA)	$\times 10^{-9}$	n
micro	1 millionth	$\times 10^{-6}$	μ
milli	1 thousandth	$\times 10^{-3}$	m
centi	1 hundredth	$\times 10^{-2}$	c
deci	1 tenth	$\times 10^{-1}$	d
deca	ten times (tenfold)	$\times 10$	da

hecto	hundred times (hundredfold)	$\times 10^2$	h
kilo	thousand times (thousandfold)	$\times 10^3$	k
mega	million times (millionfold)	$\times 10^6$	M
giga	thousand million times billion (USA)	$\times 10^9$	G
tera	billion times trillion (USA)	$\times 10^{12}$	T
peta	thousand million times quadrillion (USA)	$\times 10^{15}$	P
exa	trillion times quintillion (USA)	$\times 10^{18}$	E

Conversion: Imperial and metric measurement

Abbreviations of linear, square and cubic measurement

Metric
mm = millimetre
cm = centimetre
dm = decimetre
m = metre
dcm = decametre
hm = hectometre
km = kilometre
myr = myriametre

Imperial
in = inch
ft = foot
yd = yard
ch = chain
fur = furlong
m = mile

Linear measurement

Metric	Imperial	Imperial	Metric
10 mm = cm	= 0.3937 in	1 in	= 2.5400 cm
10 cm = 1 dm	= 3.9370 in	12 in = 1 ft	= 0.3048 m
10 dm = 1 m	= 39.3700 in	3 ft = 1 yd	= 0.9144 m
10 m = 1 dcm	= 32.8083 ft	22 yd = 1 ch	= 20.1168 m
10 dcm = 1 hm	= 10.93610 yd	10 ch = 1 fur	= 0.2012 km
10 hm = 1 km	= 0.6213 m	8 fur = 1 m	= 1.6093 km
10 km = 1 myr	= 6.2137 m		

Square measurement (area)

Metric		Imperial
100 sq mm	= 1 sq cm	= 0.1550 sq in
100 sq cm	= 1 sq dm	= 15.5000 sq in
100 sq dm	= 1 sq m	= 1.1960 sq yd
100 sq m	= 1 are	= 0.0247 acres
100 ares	= 1 hectare	= 2.4710 acres
100 hectares	= 1 sq km	= 0.3862 sq m

Imperial		Metric
1 sq in		= 6.4516 sq cm
144 sq in	= 1 sq ft	= 0.0929 sq m
9 sq ft	= 1 sq yd	= 0.8361 sq m
4840 sq yd	= 1 acre	= 0.4047 hectares
648 acres	= sq m	= 262.228 hectares

Cubic measurement (volume)

Metric		Imperial
1 cu mm		= 0.00006 cu in
1000 cu mm	= 1 cu cm	= 0.06102 cu in
1000 cu cm	= 1 cu dm	= 0.03532 cu ft
1000 cu dm	= 1 cu m	= 35.315 cu ft

Imperial		Metric
1 cu in		= 16.3871 cu cm
1728 cu in	= 1 cu ft	= 0.028317 cu m
27 cu ft	= 1 cu yd	= 0.76455 cu m

Land measurement: Gunter's Chain

Imperial		Metric
1 link	= 7.92 in	= 0.2012 m
25 links	= 1 pole, rod or perch	= 5.0292 m
100 links	= 1 ch (22 yds)	= 20.1168 m
10 ch	= 1 fur	= 0.2012 km
80 ch	= 1 m	= 1.6096 km

Abbreviations of avoirdupois weight (mass)

Metric	Imperial
mg = milligram	**gr** = grain
cg = centigram	**dr** = dram
dg = decigram	**oz** = ounce
g = gram	**lb** = pound
dag = decagram	**st** = stone
hg = hectogram	**qr** = quarter
kg = kilogram	**cwt** = hundredweight
Mg = megagram	**ton**
tonne	

Metric		**Imperial**
1mg		= 0.0154 gr
10 mg	**= 1 cg**	= 0.1543 gr
10 cg	**= 1 dg**	= 1.5432 gr
10 dg	**= 1 g**	= 0.5644 dr
10 g	**= 1 dag**	= 5.6438 dr
10 dag	**= 1 hg**	= 3.5274 oz
10 hg	**= 1kg**	= 2.2046 lb
1000 kg	**= 1 Mg**	
	= (1 tonne)	} = 0.9842 ton, long

Imperial		**Metric**
1 gr		= 0.0656 g
1 dr		= 1.7718 g
16 dr	**= 1 oz**	= 28.3498 g
16 oz	**= 1 lb**	= 0.04536 kg
14lbs	**= 1 st**	= 6.35 kg
2 st	**= 1 qr**	= 12.701 kg
4 qr	**= 1 cwt**	= 50.8023 kg
20 cwt	**= 1 ton, long**	= 1.0160 tonnes

Note: 1 ton, short (USA) = 2,000 lb (UK) = 0.907 tonnes

Abbreviations of capacity

Metric		Imperial	
ml	= millilitre	fl dr	= fluid drachm
cl	= centilitre	fl oz	= fluid ounce
dl	= decilitre	gill	= gill
l	= litre	pt	= pint
dal	= decalitre	qt	= quart
hl	= hectolitre	gal	= gallon
kl	= kilolitre	bu	= bushel

Capacity

Metric		Imperial
1 ml		= 0.007 gill
10 ml	= 1 cl	= 0.0704 gill
10 cl	= 1 dl	= 0.1760 pt
10 dl	= 1 l	= 1.7598 pt
10 l	= 1 dal	= 2.1997 gal
10 dal	= 1 hl	= 2.7496 bu
10 hl	= 1 kl	= 6.1103 barrels (3.44 qr)

Imperial		Metric
60 min	= 1 fl dr	= 3.5516 ml
8 fl dr	= 1 fl oz	= 28.431 m
5 fl oz	= 1 gill	= 1.4200 dl
4 gill	= 1 pt	= 0.5683 l
2 pt	= 1 qt	= 1.1364 l
4 qt	= 1 gal	= 4.5461 l
2 gal	= 1 peck	= 9.0922 l
4 peck	= 1 bu	= 36.1888 l
8 bu	= 1 qr	= 2.9095 hl
36 gal	= 1 barrel, bulk	= 1.6366 hl

Capacity and volume (Imperial)

Capacity   Volume

1 oz	= 1.8047 cu in
1 pt	= 28.875 cu in
1 gal	= 231.000 cu in
1 barrel	= 5.6146 cu ft

Dry capacity and volume (Imperial)

Capacity   Volume

1 pt	= 33.6003 cu in
1 qt	= 67.2006 cu in
1 gal	= 268.8025 cu in
1 bu	= 1.2445 cu ft

Capacity (USA)

USA		Metric
1 min		= 0.0616 ml
60 min	= 1 fl dr	= 3.6967 ml
8 fl dr	= 1 fl oz	= 29.5735 ml
4 fl oz	= 1 gill	= 0.1183 l
4 gills	= 1 pt	= 0.4732 l
2 pt	= 1 qt	= 0.9464 l
4 qt	= 1 gal	= 3.7854 l

Weight of water

1 l	= 1 kg
1 cu m	= 1 m tonne
1 gal (UK)	= 10.022 lbs

Miscellaneous measurements (UK)

Beer

1 nip	= ¼ pt
1 small	= ½ pt
1 large	= 1 pt

1 flagon	= 1 qt = 2 pt
1 pin	= 4½ gal = 36 pt
1 six	= 6 gal = 48 pt
1 firkin	= 2 pins = 9 gal.
1 anker	= 10 gal
1 kilderkin	= 18 gal = 2 firkins
1 barrel	= 36 gal = 2 kilderkins
1 hogshead	= 54 gal = 3 kilderkins
1 puncheon	= 72 gal = 2 barrels
1 pipe (butt)	= 108 gal = 2 hogsheads
1 tun	= 216 gal = 2 pipes

Note: 1 gal (USA) = 0.832628 gal (UK)
1 barrel, petroleum (USA) = 42 gal (USA) = 34.97 gal (UK)

Wines and spirits

1 tot	= $\frac{1}{6}$ gill (in public houses) or $\frac{1}{3}$ or $\frac{1}{4}$ gill
1 noggin	= 1 gill = $\frac{1}{4}$ pt
1 bottle	= $1\frac{1}{3}$ pt

Champagne

2 bottles	= 1 magnum
2 magnums	= 1 jeroboam
5 jeroboams	= 1 nebuchadnezzar

Timber

Imperial		Metric
1 board ft	= $\frac{1}{12}$ cu ft	= 2.36 cu dm
1 cord ft	= 16 cu ft	= 0.435 cu m
1 cord	= 123 cu ft, piled	= 3.625 cu m
1 fathom	= 216 cu ft, piled	= 6.116 cu m
1 stack	= 180 cu ft	= 5.097 cu m
1 standard, London	= 270 cu ft, piled	= 7.6455 cu m
1 standard, Petrograd	= 165 cu ft, piled	= 4.6273 cu m

Angular measurement

60 seconds = 1 minute
60 minutes = 1 degree (1°)
90 degrees = 1 quadrant (right angle)
4 quadrants = 1 circle (360°)

Nautical measurement (UK)

1 span	= 9 in (22.86 cm)
8 spans	= 6 ft (1.8288 m)
6 ft	= 1 fathom
100 fathoms	= 1 cable (182.88 m)
10 cables	= 1 nautical mile
	= 6,080 feet (1.8553 km)
3 nautical m	= 1 league (5.5659 km)
60 nautical m	= 1 degree of longitude

Note: 1 international nautical mile = 6,076.1 ft (1.853 km)

Velocity

In the metric system, velocity is measured as metres per second. This is written either as m/s or ms^{-1}.

Conversion

	m/s	ft/sec	mile/hr	km/hr
1 metre/second	1.0	3.28084	2.23694	3.6
1 foot/second	0.3048	1.0	0.681817	1.091
1 mile/hour	0.44704	1.46667	1.0	1.61
1 kilometre/hour	0.277778	0.911346	0.621371	1.0

To convert mph to km/hr, multiply by 1.609344.
For quick conversion, multiply by 8, divide by 5:

    10 mph × 8 = 80 ÷ 5
               = 16 km/hr

To convert m/s to ft/s, multiply by 3.280840.
To convert ft/s to m/s, multiply by 0.3048.

To convert km/hr to mph, multiply by 0.621371
For quick conversion, multiply by 5, divide by 8:

$$16 \text{ km/hr} \times 5 = 80 \div 8$$
$$= 10 \text{ mph}$$

Conversion of mph to km/hr

mph	km/hr	km/hr	mph
1	1.610	1	0.621
5	8.047	5	3.107
10	16.093	10	6.214
15	24.140	15	9.321
20	32.187	20	12.427
25	40.234	25	15.534
30	48.280	30	18.641
35	56.327	35	21.748
40	64.374	40	24.855
45	72.421	45	27.962
50	80.467	50	31.069
55	88.514	55	34.175
60	96.561	60	37.282
65	104.607	65	40.389
70	112.651	70	43.496
75	120.701	75	46.603
80	128.748	80	49.710
85	136.794	85	52.817
90	144.841	90	55.923
95	152.888	95	59.030
100	160.934	100	62.137
105	168.981	105	65.243
110	177.028	110	68.351
115	185.075	115	71.458
120	193.121	120	74.465
125	201.168	125	77.671
130	209.215	130	80.778
135	217.261	135	83.885
140	225.308	140	86.992
145	233.355	145	90.099
150	241.402	150	93.206
155	249.448	155	96.313

160	257.495	160	94.420
165	265.542	165	102.526
170	273.588	170	105.633
175	281.635	175	108.740
180	289.682	180	111.847
185	297.729	185	114.954
190	305.775	190	118.061
195	313.870	195	121.167
200	321.870	200	124.274

Average speed

To find average speed, divide distance travelled by the time taken, as:

> If a car travels 180 miles in 6 hours,
> average speed $= 180 \div 6$
> $\qquad\qquad\quad = 30$ mph

Velocity of light and sound

Speed of light $= 2.997925 \times 10^8$ m/s
$\qquad\qquad\;\; = 1.079253 \times 10^9$ km/hr $= 186,281$ m/s
Speed of sound $= 340.294$ m/s $= 1116.45$ ft/s

Fraction and decimal equivalents (to 4 decimal places)

Fraction	Decimal	Fraction	Decimal
$\frac{1}{2}$	.5000	$\frac{5}{9}$	.5555
$\frac{1}{3}$	.3333	$\frac{6}{9}=\frac{2}{3}$	
$\frac{2}{3}$	.6667	$\frac{7}{9}$	.7777
$\frac{1}{4}$	.2500	$\frac{8}{9}$	.8888
$\frac{3}{4}$	.7500	$\frac{1}{10}$	.1000
$\frac{1}{5}$	.2000	$\frac{2}{10}=\frac{1}{5}$	
$\frac{2}{5}$	.4000	$\frac{3}{10}$	.3000
$\frac{3}{5}$	.6000	$\frac{4}{10}=\frac{2}{5}$	
$\frac{4}{5}$	.8000	$\frac{5}{10}=\frac{1}{2}$	
$\frac{1}{6}$	.1667	$\frac{6}{10}=\frac{3}{5}$	
$\frac{2}{6}=\frac{1}{3}$		$\frac{7}{10}$	.7000
$\frac{3}{6}=\frac{1}{2}$		$\frac{8}{10}=\frac{4}{5}$	
$\frac{4}{6}=\frac{2}{3}$		$\frac{9}{10}$	.9000
$\frac{5}{6}$	.8833	$\frac{1}{11}$	.0909
$\frac{1}{7}$	.1429	$\frac{2}{11}$	.1818
$\frac{2}{7}$	.2858	$\frac{3}{11}$	.2727
$\frac{3}{7}$	.4287	$\frac{4}{11}$	.3636
$\frac{4}{7}$	.5716	$\frac{5}{11}$	.4545
$\frac{5}{7}$	.7245	$\frac{6}{11}$	.5454
$\frac{6}{7}$	.8674	$\frac{7}{11}$	.6363
$\frac{1}{8}$	.1250	$\frac{8}{11}$	.7272
$\frac{2}{8}=\frac{1}{4}$		$\frac{9}{11}$	.8181
$\frac{3}{8}$	.3750	$\frac{10}{11}$	.9090
$\frac{4}{8}=\frac{1}{2}$		$\frac{1}{12}$	.0833
$\frac{5}{8}$	.6250	$\frac{2}{12}=\frac{1}{6}$	
$\frac{6}{8}=\frac{3}{4}$		$\frac{3}{12}=\frac{1}{4}$	
$\frac{7}{8}$	.8750	$\frac{4}{12}=\frac{1}{3}$	
$\frac{1}{9}$	.1111	$\frac{5}{12}$	.4166
$\frac{2}{9}$	.2222	$\frac{6}{12}=\frac{1}{2}$	
$\frac{3}{9}=\frac{1}{3}$		$\frac{7}{12}$	.5832
$\frac{4}{9}$	.4444	$\frac{8}{12}=\frac{2}{3}$	

Fraction	Decimal	Fraction	Decimal
$\frac{9}{12} = \frac{3}{4}$		$\frac{15}{16}$	.9375
$\frac{10}{12} = \frac{5}{6}$		$\frac{1}{20}$	.0500
$\frac{11}{12}$	.9165	$\frac{1}{21}$	.0476
$\frac{1}{13}$	.0769	$\frac{1}{22}$	.0455
$\frac{1}{14}$	.0714	$\frac{1}{23}$	.0435
$\frac{1}{15}$	.0667	$\frac{1}{24}$	.0417
$\frac{2}{15}$	.1334	$\frac{1}{25}$	.0400
$\frac{3}{15} = \frac{1}{5}$		$\frac{1}{30}$	.0333
$\frac{4}{15}$	.2668	$\frac{1}{32}$	.0313
$\frac{5}{15} = \frac{1}{3}$		$\frac{2}{32} = \frac{1}{16}$	
$\frac{6}{15} = \frac{2}{5}$		$\frac{3}{32}$	.0939
$\frac{7}{15}$	.4669	$\frac{4}{32} = \frac{1}{8}$	
$\frac{8}{15}$	.5336	$\frac{5}{32}$	.1565
$\frac{9}{15} = \frac{3}{5}$		$\frac{6}{32} = \frac{3}{16}$	
$\frac{10}{15} = \frac{2}{3}$		$\frac{7}{32}$	.2191
$\frac{11}{15}$	.7337	$\frac{8}{32} = \frac{1}{4}$	
$\frac{12}{15} = \frac{4}{5}$		$\frac{9}{32}$	.2817
$\frac{13}{15}$	.8671	$\frac{10}{32} = \frac{5}{16}$	
$\frac{14}{15}$	.9338	$\frac{11}{32}$	.3443
$\frac{1}{16}$	.0625	$\frac{12}{32} = \frac{3}{8}$	
$\frac{2}{16} = \frac{1}{8}$		$\frac{13}{32}$	.4069
$\frac{3}{16}$	.1875	$\frac{14}{32} = \frac{7}{16}$	
$\frac{4}{16} = \frac{1}{4}$		$\frac{15}{32}$	.4695
$\frac{5}{16}$	.3125	$\frac{16}{32} = \frac{1}{2}$	
$\frac{6}{16} = \frac{3}{8}$		$\frac{17}{32}$	.5321
$\frac{7}{16}$	.4375	$\frac{18}{32} = \frac{9}{16}$	
$\frac{8}{16} = \frac{1}{2}$		$\frac{19}{32}$	.5947
$\frac{9}{16}$	.5625	$\frac{20}{32} = \frac{5}{8}$	
$\frac{10}{16} = \frac{5}{8}$		$\frac{21}{32}$	.6573
$\frac{11}{16}$	.6875	$\frac{22}{32} = \frac{11}{16}$	
$\frac{12}{16} = \frac{3}{4}$		$\frac{23}{32}$	.7199
$\frac{13}{16}$	.8125	$\frac{24}{32} = \frac{3}{4}$	
$\frac{14}{16} = \frac{7}{8}$			

Fraction	Decimal
$\frac{25}{32}$	.7813
$\frac{27}{32}$	.8451
$\frac{28}{32} = \frac{7}{8}$	
$\frac{29}{32}$	.9077
$\frac{30}{32} = \frac{15}{16}$	
$\frac{31}{32}$	.9703
$\frac{1}{33}$	.0303
$\frac{1}{34}$	.0294
$\frac{1}{35}$	.0286
$\frac{1}{40}$	.0250
$\frac{1}{45}$	.0222
$\frac{1}{50}$	.0200
$\frac{1}{55}$	.0182
$\frac{1}{60}$	.0167
$\frac{1}{65}$	.0154
$\frac{1}{70}$	.0143
$\frac{1}{75}$	.0133
$\frac{1}{80}$	.0125
$\frac{1}{85}$	.0118
$\frac{1}{90}$	.0111
$\frac{1}{95}$	.0105
$\frac{1}{100}$	.0100
$\frac{1}{500}$	.0020
$\frac{1}{1000}$	.0010
$\frac{1}{10000}$	.0001

International paper sizes

The basis of international paper sizes is a rectangle with
an area of 1 square metre with sides in the proportion of
$1:\sqrt{2}$ (1:1.414...). However large the sheet, the proportion
always remains the same.

Designation	Metric size (mm)	Imperial size (in)
A0	841 × 1189	33.11 × 46.81
A1	594 × 841	23.39 × 33.11
A2	420 × 594	16.54 × 23.39
A3	297 × 420	11.69 × 16.54
A4	210 × 297	8.27 × 11.69
A5	148 × 210	5.83 × 8.27
A6	105 × 148	4.13 × 5.83
A7	74 × 105	2.91 × 4.13
A8	52 × 74	2.05 × 2.91
A9	37 × 52	1.46 × 2.05
A10	26 × 37	1.02 × 1.46
B0	1000 × 1414	39.37 × 55.67
B1	707 × 1000	27.83 × 39.37
B2	500 × 707	19.68 × 27.83
B3	353 × 500	13.90 × 19.68
B4	250 × 353	9.84 × 13.90
B5	176 × 250	6.93 × 9.84
B6	125 × 176	4.92 × 6.93
B7	88 × 125	3.46 × 4.92
B8	62 × 88	2.44 × 3.46
B9	44 × 62	1.73 × 2.44
B10	31 × 44	1.23 × 1.73

Note: The A series is used for writing paper, books and magazines. The B series is used for larger items such as wallcharts and posters.

Quantities of paper

Writing paper
24 sheets = 1 quire
20 quires = 1 ream = 480 sheets

Printer's paper
516 sheets = 1 ream
2 reams = 1 bundle
= 1032 sheets
5 bundles = 1 bale = 5160 sheets

5 | LANGUAGES

Alphabets

Alphabets are collections of symbols arranged in a particular order to represent the sounds made in human speech. The word comes from *alpha* and *beta*, the first two letters of the Greek alphabet.

The earliest forms of alphabets were pictograms with figures of animals or birds to convey a special sound. Just as happened in the development of numerals, the early alphabets were clumsy and writing anything took a long time, but gradually they were simplified. The Egyptians, for instance, used pictograms, then hieroglyphic, hieratic and demotic scripts. This went on from about 2,700 BC to 700 BC. The last alphabet before the introduction of Arabic was Coptic script which used the Greek alphabet and added new letters, many of them vowels.

Although the origin of the modern alphabet is attributed to the Phoenicians, the Sumerians were writing on clay tablets with reed pens by about 2,000 BC, and there was at the same time a Semitic alphabet consisting of 22 letters used in Syria and by many Semitic people.

What the Phoenicians did was to hand on their alphabet to the Greeks. In its final form the Greek alphabet consisted of 24 letters and is still the basis of modern Greek and Russian alphabets.

Then the Romans took it over and they too made modifications, so that their alphabet had 22 letters. Wherever the Romans went, their alphabet went with them. They invaded England and in time the Anglo-Saxons began to use it but some changes were made. Letters representing hard and soft 'th' were introduced; later still J, U and W were developed.

Eastern countries have much longer alphabets, but in many countries these are now being simplified.

Some important languages

No one knows just how many languages there are in the

world. Estimates vary from 3,000–4,500, much depending on whether or not dialects are included. Dialects are variations of an official language spoken in particular regions, but when millions of people use a dialect – as happens in China – some experts regard it as a separate language.

In Nigeria, for instance, there are so many separate languages and hundreds of dialects that the 'official' language is English.

Language	Speakers (millions)	Region
Chinese		
Guoyu	700	Guoyu is standardised.
Cantonese	55	Northern Chinese, spoken in
Wu	40	mainland China, Hong Kong
Fukien	40	and many parts of south-east Asia.
English	395	UK, USA, Ireland, Australia, Canada, New Zealand, Nigeria, many parts of the Commonwealth; joint official language in others, e.g. Kenya, Malta.
Russian		
Great Russian	250	there are about 110 other
Ukranian	40	languages and dialects in the USSR.

А Б В Г Д Ё Ж З Й К
Л М Н О П Р С Т У Ф
Х Ц Ч Ш Ъ Ы Ь Э Ю Я а б в г д ё ж з
й к л м н о п р с т у
ф х ц ч ш ъ ы ь э ю я

Spanish	235	Spain, many South American countries, e.g.

		Argentina, Bolivia, Central America, Philippines, Puerto Rico.
Hindustani	230	India has over 840 languages; Hindustani is spoken by more than 25% of Indians, also spoken in parts of Pakistan.
Bengali	140	north-east India, Bangladesh.
Arabic	140	most of the Middle East including Egypt, Somalia, Sudan, Lebanon, Saudi Arabia, Syria and in Tunisia.
Portuguese	135	Portugal, Brazil and former colonies such as Angola, Mozambique and Goa.
German	120	Germany, Austria, Liechtenstein, Luxemburg, Switzerland and former colonies in Africa.
Japanese	110	Japan, Taiwan, Hawaii, parts of south-east Asia.
French	95	France, Switzerland, Monaco, Luxemburg, Belgium, French Pacific territories, parts of Canada, former colonies in Africa.
Indonesia	95	actually Malay-Indonesian; Indonesia, and Malaysia but many other languages and dialects, southern Thailand, Sarawak.
Italian	60	Italy, Switzerland, Libya, Eritrea and in former colonies.
Punjabi	40–70	Punjab in India, parts of Pakistan.
Urdu	60	parts of India, parts of Bangladesh and Pakistan.
Korean	55	North Korea, South Korea.

6 | RELIGION

Only estimates can be made of the number of people who belong to the various religions. Many claim to belong to a religion but never practise it, although they might live by its principles.

● Only the most important places where religions flourish are given below. As peoples emigrate to other countries, so they take their religions with them; but it is impossible to list all the countries that have substantial religious minorities living there.

Some important religions

Religion	Numbers (millions)	Region
Christian	1,050	Europe, N. and S. and Central America, Australasia, central and east Africa, Greece, many parts of south-east Asia.
Islam (Muslim)	600	most of Middle East, parts of North Africa, central and east Africa, Indonesia, many other parts of south-east Asia.
Hindu	465	India, parts of Pakistan, part of Sri Lanka.
Buddhist	250	India, parts of Indo-China, China and Japan and elsewhere in south-east Asia.
Confucian	155	China, Japan, other parts of south-east Asia
Shinto	35	Japan.
Taoist	20	China, some practising in Japan.
Jewish	18	Israel, many other parts of the world.

7 | FIGUREMANIA

Usually people groan when they have to work out sums.
They automatically reach for their calculators even though
they have been taught how to do long multiplication and
long division sums at school. There are times, though,
when there might not be a calculator handy and, anyway,
everyone should have some idea of what the answer should
be in case they press the wrong button.

There are ways of working out the answers to some
sums very quickly. Indeed, some – like multiplying by 11 –
are faster than using a calculator.

You might think that the methods shown in this
section of the book are rather complicated. But that's not
so. If you follow a couple of examples by working them
through step by step, you'll find that some of the steps can
be cut out and in many cases you'll find you can just write
down the answer.

There are a few for you to try – the answers to them are
in the back of this section.

Millions and millions of millions

People are often confused when they hear words like
millions and billions being used, since there are different
systems in operation. For instance, the UK and Germany
use one system, the USA and France another.

In the UK a billion is a million million; in the USA it is
a thousand million. In the UK a trillion is a million million
million; in the USA it is a million million and is therefore
the equivalent of a UK billion.

It should be noted that there is a tendency to adopt the
American and French terminology, but this is still
unofficial.

The differences are best expressed by the factors used.

Name	Factor (UK)	Factor (USA)
million	$\times 10^6$	$\times 10^6$
billion	$\times 10^{12}$	$\times 10^9$
trillion	$\times 10^{18}$	$\times 10^{12}$
quadrillion	$\times 10^{24}$	$\times 10^{15}$
sextillion	$\times 10^{36}$	$\times 10^{21}$
septillion	$\times 10^{42}$	$\times 10^{24}$
octillion	$\times 10^{48}$	$\times 10^{27}$
nonillion	$\times 10^{54}$	$\times 10^{30}$
decillion	$\times 10^{60}$	$\times 10^{33}$
centillion	$\times 10^{600}$	$\times 10^{330}$

Multiplication by multiples of 10

Almost everyone knows that to multiply any number by 10, 100, 1,000, 10,000 and so on, all you have to do is to add the identical number of noughts to arrive at the answer:

$$123 \times 100 = 12,300$$
$$456 \times 1,000 = 456,000$$

This makes the multiplication by some other numbers which are related to 10 very simple:

× 5, add 1 nought, divide by 2	674×5	$= 6,740 \div 2$ $= 3,370$
× 25, add 2 noughts, divide by 4	$1,236 \times 25$	$= 123,600 \div 4$ $= 30,900$
× 50, add 2 noughts, divide by 2	$4,681 \times 50$	$= 468,100 \div 2$ $= 234,050$
× 125, add 3 noughts, divide by 8	124×125	$= 124,000 \div 8$ $= 15,500$
× 250, add 3 noughts, divide by 4	42×250	$= 42,000 \div 4$ $= 10,500$

Multiplication by numbers close to but lower than 100s

17 × 98 = 1,666:

Steps

(a) Subtract 98 from nearest hundred	100 − 98	= 2
(b) Multiply 17 × 100	17 × 100	= 1,700 −
(c) Multiply 17 × 2, subtract result from previous answer	17 × 2	= 34
		1,666

15 × 196 = 2,940:

Steps

(a) Subtract 196 from nearest hundred	200 − 196	= 4
(b) Multiply 15 × 200	15 × 200	= 3000 −
(c) Multiply 15 × 4, subtract result from previous answer	15 × 4	= 60
		2,940

13 × 297 = 3,861:

(a)	= 3
(b)	= 3900 −
(c)	= 39
	3,861

Problems

1. 19 × 99
2. 13 × 297
3. 52 × 496

Multiplication by 11

To multiply 2 figures by 11

This is a remarkable method of multiplying. You will see that you have to find the sum of the 2 figures. If the answer is greater than 9, put down the unit in the answer, carry the 10 and add it to the number on the left.

52 × 11 = 572:

Steps

(a) Separate 5 and 2, leave a space   52 × 11   = 5   2

(b) Add 5 and 2, put the answer in the space   5 + 2   = 7 = 572

84 × 11 = 924:

Steps

(a) Separate 8 and 4, leave a space   84 × 11   = 8   4

(b) Add 8 and 4, put unit in space, carry the 10 to the left-hand figure   8 + 4   = 12 = 924

93 × 11 = 1,023:

Steps

(a) Separate 9 and 3, leave a space   93 × 11   = 9   3

(b) Add 9 and 3, put unit in space, carry the 10 to the left-hand figure   9 + 3   = 12 = 1,023

76 × 11 = 836

(a)   = 7   6

(b)   = 836

Problems

4. 24 × 11
5. 63 × 11
6. 55 × 11
7. 84 × 11
8. 96 × 11

To multiply 3 or more figures by 11

This might look slightly more complicated than multiplying only 2 figures by 11, but really it is just as simple and quick to do. Again, if the sum of 2 numbers is greater than 9, put the unit in the answer and carry the 10 to the next figure on the left.

423 × 11 = 4,653:

Steps

(a) Put down the unit in the unit space in the answer	423 × 11	=	3
(b) Start from the right. Add each number in turn to its left-hand neighbour. Put the result in the next space on the left in the answer.	3 + 2	= 5 =	53
	2 + 4	= 6 =	653
	4 + 0	= 4 =	4,653

364 × 11 = 4,004:

Steps

(a) Put down the unit in the unit space in the answer	364 × 11	=	4
(b) Start from the right. Add each number in turn to its left-hand neighbour. Put the result in the next space on the left in the answer.	4 + 6	= 10 =	04
	6 + 3 + carry 1	= 10 =	004
	3 + 0 + carry 1	= 4 =	4,004

1642 × 11 = 18,062:

(a)	1642 × 11	=	2
(b)	2 + 4	= 6 =	62
	4 + 6	= 10 =	062
	6 + 1 +		
	carry 1	= 8 =	8,062
	1 + 0	= 1 =	18,062

Problems

9. 523 × 11
10. 614 × 11
11. 274 × 11
12. 12,356 × 11

Multiplication by 12

This is an alternative method of multiplying by 12. It's easy to follow and fast to do. Remember that if the answer to any part of the process is greater than 9, you must carry the 10s number to the next stage:

4,124 × 12 = 49,488:

Steps

(a) Put 0 in front of the number to be multiplied   04124

(b) Multiply the unit by 2, write down the answer in the unit column

$$2 × 4 = \qquad\qquad 8$$

(c) Multiply each of the following figures in turn by 2, add to the digit on the right, put down the answer

$$2 × 2 + 4 = 8 = \qquad 88$$
$$2 × 1 + 2 = 4 = \qquad 488$$
$$2 × 4 + 1 = 9 = \quad 9,488$$
$$2 × 0 + 4 = 4 = 49,488$$

6,293 × 12 = 75,516:

Steps

(a) Put 0 in front of the number to be multiplied

06293

(b) Multiply the unit by 2, write down the answer in the unit column

(c) Multiply each of the following figures in turn by 2, add to the figure on the right, put down the answer

$$= 6$$
$$2 \times 9 + 3 = 21 = 16$$
$$2 \times 2 + 9 = 15 = 516$$
$$+ \text{ carry } 2$$
$$2 \times 6 + 2 = 15 = 5,516$$
$$+ \text{ carry } 1$$
$$2 \times 0 + 6 = 7 = 75,516$$
$$+ \text{ carry } 1$$

$7,216 \times 12 = 86,592$:

(a)

07216

(b)

(c)

$$= 2$$
$$2 \times 1 + 6 = 92$$
$$+ \text{ carry } 1$$
$$2 \times 2 + 1 = 592$$
$$2 \times 7 + 2 = 6,592$$
$$2 \times 0 + 7 = 86,592$$
$$+ \text{ carry } 1$$

Problems

13. $2,312 \times 12$
14. $5,412 \times 12$
15. $17,486 \times 12$

The Russian method of multiplication

It is said that this method of multiplication was invented by Russian peasants who knew very little about mathematics. They could add and subtract, multiply and divide by 2, but they could manage little else. This is another way of doing long multiplication:

$43 \times 29 = 1,247$:

Steps

(a)	Put 43 in one column, 29 in the other.	43	29
(b)	Divide the numbers in the left-hand column by 2, ignore remainders. At the same time, double the numbers in the right-hand column.	21 ~~10~~ 5 ~~2~~	58 ~~116~~ 232 ~~464~~
(c)	Continue until 1 is reached on the left.	1	928
(d)	Cross out all even numbers on the left and the corresponding number on the right.		
(e)	Add together the remaining numbers on the right. This gives the answer.		29 + 58 232 928 —— 1247

126 × 33 = 4,158:

(a) (b) (c) (d)

126	33
63	66
31	132
15	264
7	528
3	1056
1	2112

(e)

66 +
132
264
528
1056
2112
——
4,158

Problems

16. 53 × 25
17. 94 × 36
18. 82 × 24

Division by multiples of 10

The division of numbers by multiples of 10, e.g. 10, 100, 1,000, 10,000 and so on is straightforward. Count as many places to the left as there are noughts in the number you are dividing by, and put in a decimal point. This means that there are always as many figures on the right of the decimal point as there are noughts in the divisor:

$6,423 \div 10 = 642.3$ (1 nought, 1 figure to the right of the decimal point)

$5,749 \div 100 = 57.49$ (2 noughts, 2 figures to the right of the decimal point)

$72,947 \div 10000 = 7.2947$ (4 noughts, 4 figures to the right of the decimal point)

If there are not as many places to the left as there are noughts in the divisor, put as many noughts as are needed in front of the answer:

$64 \div 1000 = .064$ (3 figures needed, only 2 available, so 1 nought is placed in front of the answer)

$87 \div 10,000 = .0087$ (4 figures needed, only 2 available, so 2 noughts placed in front of the answer)

Problems

19. $295 \div 10$

20. $4,614 \div 100$

21. $928,756 \div 100,000$

22. $728 \div 10,000$

23. $9 \div 1,000$

Dividing numbers by single figures

It is possible to find out if a number can be divided exactly by single figures from 1 to 9 (excluding 7), if you use the tests shown below.

Number	Divisor	Test	Yes/No	Reason
4156	2	does the number end with an even digit?	Yes	6 is an even number.
823	3	is the sum of the digits exactly divisible by 3?	No	$8+3+3=13$; 13 is not exactly divisible by 3.
3051	3	is the sum of the digits exactly divisible by 3?	Yes	$3+0+5+1=9$; 9 is exactly divisible by 3.
2425	4	are the last 2 digits exactly divisible by 4?	No	25 is not exactly divisible by 4.
928	4	are the last 2 digits exactly divisible by 4?	Yes	28 is exactly divisible by 4.
7125	5	is the last digit a 0 or a 5?	Yes	7125 ends with 5.
558	5	is the last digit a 0 or a 5?	No	558 does not end with a 0 or a 5.
6246	6	is the number exactly divisible by both 2 and 3?	Yes	$6246 \div 2 = 3123$; $6246 \div 3 = 2082$.
393	6	is the number exactly divisible by both 2 and 3?	No	although 393 is exactly divisible by 3, it is not divisible by 2.
8175	8	are the last 3 digits exactly divisible by 8?	No	175 is not exactly divisible by 8.
5880	8	are the last three digits exactly divisible by 8?	Yes	$880 \div 8 = 110$.
3991	9	is the sum of the digits exactly divisible by 9?	No	$3+9+9+1=22$; 22 is not exactly divisible by 9.
3447	9	is the sum of the digits exactly divisible by 9?	Yes	$3+4+4+7=18$; 18 is exactly divisible by 9.

Problems

24. Is 2,143 exactly divisible by 2?
25. Is 596 exactly divisible by 3?
26. Is 904 exactly divisible by 4?
27. Is 902 exactly divisible by 5?
28. Is 2,460 exactly divisible by 6?
29. Is 32,168 exactly divisible by 8?
30. Is 4,219 exactly divisible by 9?
31. Is 7,299 exactly divisible by 9?
32. Is 54,064 exactly divisible by 8?
33. Is 5,174 exactly divisible by 2?
34. Is 4,154 exactly divisible by 6?
35. Is 3,432 exactly divisible by 3?
36. Is 20,202 exactly divisible by 5?
37. Is 90,005 exactly divisible by 5?
38. Is 1,416 exactly divisible by 4?

Dividing by factors

People often make mistakes when doing long division sums. If you can break the divisor down into two simple factors, you can use short division instead, so mistakes will be much less likely:

461,823 ÷ 28 = 16,493 remainder 19

Steps

(a) Write down the factors of 28

$7 \times 4 = 28$ ∴ 7 and 4 are the factors of 28

(b) Divide the number by 7

7)461,823

  69,574 remainder 5 (units)

(c) Divide the answer by 4

4)69,574

  16,493 remainder 2 (units)

(d) 16,493 is the answer; the remainder is the result of multiplying the last remainder by the first

$2 \times 7 = 14 + 5 = 19$

divisor and adding the first
remainder to it

(e) Final answer: 16,493
remainder 19.

32,914 ÷ 56 = 587 remainder 42

Steps

(a) Write down the factors $8 \times 7 = 56$
   of 56

(b) Divide the number by 8   8│32,914

(c) Divide the answer by 7   7│ 4,114 remainder 2
                                587 remainder 5

(d) 587 is the answer, now find
   the remainder $5 \times 8 = 40 + 2 = 42$

(e) Final answer: 587
   remainder 42.

91,672 ÷ 48 = 1,909 remainder 40

(a) $6 \times 8 = 48$
(b)   6│91,672
(c)   8│15,278 remainder 4
                               1,909 remainder 6
(d) $6 \times 6 + 4 = 40$
(e) Final answer: 1909
   remainder 40.

Problems

39. 69,714 ÷ 15
40. 45,674 ÷ 21
41. 69,253 ÷ 42
42. 576,284 ÷ 49

Dividing numbers from 100—889 by 95—99

Division of 100s by 99

This is simple:
100 ÷ 99 = 1 remainder 1
200 ÷ 99 = 2 remainder 2

$300 \div 99 = 3$ remainder 3, etc. If you use this information, the division of other numbers by 99 becomes very easy:

$726 \div 99 = 7$ remainder 33:

Steps

(a) Divide the hundreds by 99

$700 \div 99 = 7$
remainder 7
remainder $7 + 26 = 33$

(b) 7 is the answer; the final remainder is the result of adding the remainder 7 to the unused figures in the original number

(c) Final answer: 7 remainder 33.

$829 \div 99 = 8$ remainder 37

(a) Divide the hundreds by 99

$800 \div 99 = 8$
remainder 8
remainder $8 + 29 = 37$

(b) 8 is the answer; the final remainder is the result of adding the remainder 7 to the unused figures in the original number

(c) Final answer: 8 remainder 37.

$888 \div 99 = 8$ remainder 96

(a)

$= 8$ remainder 8

(b)

$= 8 + 88 = 96$

(c) Final answer: 8 remainder 96.

Problems
_____

43. $524 \div 99$
44. $683 \div 99$
45. $748 \div 99$
46. $1,240 \div 99$

Division by 98

This is a similar method as that for dividing by 99.

524 ÷ 98 = 5 remainder 34

Steps

(a) Divide the hundreds by 98 but double the remainder

(b) 5 is the answer; the final remainder is the result of adding remainder 10 to the unused figures in the original number

(c) Final answer: 5 remainder 34.

$524 \div 98 = 5$
remainder $5 \times 2 = 10$
remainder $10 + 24 = 34$

648 ÷ 98 = 6 remainder 60

(a) Divide the hundreds by 98 but double the remainder

(b) 6 is the answer; the final remainder is the result of adding remainder 12 to the unused figures in the original number

(c) Final answer: 6 remainder 60.

$648 \div 98 = 6$
remainder $6 \times 2 = 12$
remainder $12 + 48 = 60$

476 ÷ 98 = 4 remainder 84

(a)

(b)

(c) Final answer: 4 remainder 84.

$= 4$ remainder 8
$= 8 + 76 = 84$

Problems

47. $621 \div 98$
48. $809 \div 98$
49. $1421 \div 98$

Division by 95–97

The method is similar. Remainders must be multiplied by the difference between the divisor and 100, and added to the unused figures in the original number:

When dividing by 97, multiply the remainder by 3, add to the unused figures.

When dividing by 96, multiply the remainder by 4, add to the unused figures.

When dividing by 95, multiply the remainder by 5, add to the unused figures.

Problems
_____

50. 410 ÷ 95
51. 716 ÷ 96
52. 631 ÷ 97

Ready reckoner multiplication and division table

1	2	3	4	5	6	7	8	9	10	11	12
2	4	6	8	10	12	14	16	18	20	22	24
3	6	9	12	15	18	21	24	27	30	33	36
4	8	12	16	20	24	28	32	36	40	44	48
5	10	15	20	25	30	35	40	45	50	55	60
6	12	18	24	30	36	42	48	54	60	66	72
7	14	21	28	35	42	49	56	63	70	77	84
8	16	24	32	40	48	56	64	72	80	88	96
9	18	27	36	45	54	63	72	81	90	99	108
10	20	30	40	50	60	70	80	90	100	110	120
11	22	33	44	55	66	77	88	99	110	121	132
12	24	36	48	60	72	84	96	108	120	132	144
13	26	39	52	65	78	91	104	117	130	143	156
14	28	42	56	70	84	98	112	126	140	154	168
15	30	45	60	75	90	105	120	135	150	165	180
16	32	48	64	80	96	112	128	144	160	176	192
17	34	51	68	85	102	119	136	153	170	187	204
18	36	54	72	90	108	126	144	162	180	198	216
19	38	57	76	95	114	133	152	171	190	209	228
20	40	60	80	100	120	140	160	180	200	220	240

Ready reckoner multiplication and division table

	13	14	15	16	17	18	19	20	21	22	23	24	25
13	169	182	195	208	221	234	247	260	273	286	299	312	325
14	182	196	210	224	238	252	266	280	294	308	322	336	350
15	195	210	225	240	255	270	285	300	315	330	345	360	375
16	208	224	240	256	272	288	304	320	336	352	368	384	400
17	221	238	255	272	289	306	323	340	357	374	391	408	425
18	234	252	270	288	306	324	342	360	378	396	414	432	450
19	247	266	285	304	323	342	361	380	399	418	437	456	475
20	260	280	300	320	340	360	380	400	420	440	460	480	500
21	273	294	315	336	357	378	399	420	441	462	483	504	525
22	286	308	330	352	374	396	418	440	462	484	506	528	550
23	299	322	345	368	391	414	437	460	483	506	529	552	575
24	312	336	360	384	408	432	456	480	504	528	552	576	600
25	325	350	375	400	425	450	475	500	525	550	575	600	625

To multiply 2 numbers together

(a) Look along the top line for one of the 2 numbers to be multiplied together.
(b) Look down the left-hand column for the second number.
(c) Run you fingers both down and across the columns. The answer is where they meet.

To divide one number by another

(a) Look along the top line until you find the number you are dividing by.
(b) Look down that column until you find the number you are dividing into.
(c) Run your fingers across that line to the left-hand column. That number is the answer.

Sometimes you will not find the exact number that you are dividing into, e.g. 392 ÷ 22. Take the following steps:
(a) As above, look across the top line until you find the number you are dividing by, i.e. 22.
(b) Look down that column until you find the nearest but lower number to the number you are dividing into, i.e. 374.
(c) Run your finger across that line to the left-hand column. That number is the answer, i.e. 17.
(d) Now subtract the number you found from the number you were looking for, i.e. 392−378 = 18; 18 is the remainder.
(e) The answer is 17 remainder 18

Problems

53. 23 × 22
54. 19 × 23
55. 23 × 24
56. 418 ÷ 19
57. 463 ÷ 22
58. 287 ÷ 19

Table of numbers 1–30, squares, cubes, and square and cube roots

Number	Square	Square Root	Cube	Cube Root
1	1	1.0	1	1.0
2	4	1.414	8	1.26
3	9	1.732	27	1.442
4	16	2.0	64	1.587
5	25	2.236	125	1.71
6	36	2.449	216	1.817
7	49	2.646	343	1.913
8	64	2.828	512	2.0
9	81	3.0	729	2.08
10	100	3.162	1000	2.154
11	121	3.317	1331	2.224
12	144	3.464	1728	2.289
13	169	3.606	2197	2.351
14	196	3.742	2744	2.41
15	225	3.873	3375	2.466
16	256	4.0	4096	2.52
17	289	4.123	4913	2.571
18	324	4.243	5832	2.621
19	361	4.359	6859	2.668
20	400	4.472	8000	2.714
21	441	4.583	9261	2.759
22	484	4.69	10648	2.802
23	529	4.796	12167	2.844
24	576	4.899	13824	2.885
25	625	5.0	15625	2.924
30	900	5.477	27000	3.107

Powers, indices and roots

There is a method of writing very large and very small numbers which is a kind of mathematical shorthand.

Powers and indices

Powers are the products of equal numbers. If a number is multiplied by itself, it is said to have been raised to the power of 2, and 2 is written as an index figure above the base figure:

$$5 \times 5 = 5^2$$

The power or index figure tells you how many times the base number is multiplied by itself:

$$7^4 = 7 \times 7 \times 7 \times 7$$
$$9^7 = 9 \times 9 \times 9 \times 9 \times 9 \times 9 \times 9$$

Negative powers or index figures tell you how many times the base number should be divided into 1:

$$4^{-1} = 1 \div 4 = \tfrac{1}{4}$$
$$8^{-2} = 1 \div 8 = \tfrac{1}{64}$$

Note: indices is the plural of index.

Multiplication and division of numbers with indices

Identical numbers with indices can be easily multiplied by writing down the base number in the answer and adding the indices together:

$$2^4 \times 2^3 = 2^7$$
$$6^3 \times 6^5 \times 6^2 = 6^{10}$$

Identical numbers with indices can be just as easily divided by writing down the base number and subtracting the indices:

$$8^7 \div 8^2 = 8^5$$
$$37^9 \div 37^3 = 37^6$$

Numbers in multiples of 10

Standard form is a way of writing these very large or very small numbers. The base number has to have a value of 1

to 9, and then it must be adjusted to a power of 10.
Note that:

$$100 = 10^2 \ (10 \times 10)$$
$$1{,}000 = 10^3 \ (10 \times 10 \times 10)$$
$$10{,}000 = 10^4 \ (10 \times 10 \times 10 \times 10)$$
$$100{,}000 = 10^5 \ (10 \times 10 \times 10 \times 10 \times 10)$$
$$1{,}000{,}000 = 10^6 \ (10 \times 10 \times 10 \times 10 \times 10 \times 10), \text{ and so}$$

on.

You can see that the power of 10 is equal to the number of noughts that come after the base number, in this case 1. Using this knowledge, the writing of large numbers in multiples of 10 is very simple:

$$35{,}000 = 35 \times 10^3$$
$$21{,}000{,}000 = 21 \times 10^6$$

Decimal numbers can be multiplied by a power of 10 by moving the decimal point to the right, so that the numbers of places moved corresponds to the index figure:

$$4.267 \times 10^2 = 426.7$$
$$0.92455 \times 10^4 = 9245.5$$

Decimal numbers can easily be equally divided by a power of 10 by moving the decimal point to the left so that the number of places moved corresponds to the index figure.
Note:

$$10^{-1} = 0.1 \ (1 \div 10)$$
$$10^{-2} = 0.01 \ (1 \div 10 \div 10)$$
$$10^{-3} = 0.001 \ (1 \div 10 \div 10 \div 10 \div 10)$$
$$10^{-4} = 0.0001 \ (1 \div 10 \div 10 \div 10 \div 10)$$
$$10^{-5} = 0.00001 \ (1 \div 10 \div 10 \div 10 \div 10 \div 10)$$
$$10^{-6} = 0.000001 \ (1 \div 10 \div 10 \div 10 \div 10 \div 10 \div 10), \text{ and so on.}$$

So you can see that the negative power of 10 corresponds to the number of places following the decimal point.

Multiplication of numbers in standard form

All numbers have to be written in standard form, so they must be written down with a value of 1 to 9 and adjusted to the correct power of 10:

$$20,000 = 2 \times 10^4$$
$$400,000 = 4 \times 10^5$$

If numbers are not exactly divisible by 10, use decimals:

$$3,400 = 3.4 \times 10^3$$
$$255,000 = 2.55 \times 10^5$$
$$11,600,000 = 1.16 \times 10^7$$

When working this out, you must remember that only the first number is ignored. All others count as a power of 10:

$3.8 \times 10^3 = 3,800$ (3 places following the figure 3)

$14.25 \times 10^5 = 142,500$ (5 places following the figure 1)

To multiply very large or very small numbers, rewrite them in standard form. Then multiply the figures without indices and add together the indices to the power of 10, e.g.

$$40,000 \times 700,000 = 4 \times 10^4 \times 7 \times 10^5$$
$$= 28 \times 10^9$$
$$= 2,800,000,000 \text{ (9 places following the figure 2)}$$

$$12,500 \times 25,000 = 1.25 \times 10^4 \times 2.5 \times 10^4$$
$$= 3.125 \times 10^8$$
$$= 312,500,000 \text{ (8 places following the figure 3)}$$

Roots

If a large number can be expressed as a power of a smaller number, the smaller number is called the root of the larger number:

$$9 = 3 \times 3$$
$$= 3^2$$

∴ 3 is the square root of 9 and can be written as $\sqrt{9}$

$$125 = 5 \times 5 \times 5$$
$$= 5^3$$

∴ 5 is the cube root of 125 and can be written as $\sqrt[3]{125}$ or as $125^{\frac{1}{3}}$

$$64 = 2 \times 2 \times 2 \times 2 \times 2 \times 2$$
$$= 2^6$$

∴ 2 is the sixth root of 64 and can be written as $\sqrt[6]{64}$ or as $64^{\frac{1}{6}}$

Note: square roots do not have the index number of 2, but all other roots have indices starting from 3.

Binary notation

This is a number system which uses only 2 digits, usually 1 and 0.

Base 2 is used instead of base 10 in the decimal system, so the first column on the left represents 2^0, the second on the left 2^1, the third 2^2, the fourth 2^3, the fifth 2^4 and so on.

Binary numbers from 1–20

Decimal	Binary	Decimal	Binary
1	1	11	1011
2	10	12	1100
3	11	13	1101
4	100	14	1110
5	101	15	1111
6	110	16	10000
7	111	17	10001
8	1000	18	10010
9	1001	19	10011
10	1010	20	10100

This might appear difficult, but it is simple if you:
(a) ignore all noughts
(b) remember that 1 in the right-hand column is 1
(c) remember the value of each column
(d) add all values together to find the answer

1st column on right $= 1$ $= 1$
2nd column on right $= 2^1 = 1 \times 2$ $= 2$
3rd column on right $= 2^2 = 2 \times 2$ $= 4$
4th column on right $= 2^3 = 2 \times 2 \times 2$ $= 8$
5th column on right $= 2^4 = 2 \times 2 \times 2 \times 2$ $= 16$
6th column on right $= 2^5 = 2 \times 2 \times 2 \times 2 \times 2 = 32$

Conversion from binary numbers

$2^5\ 2^4\ 2^3\ 2^2\ 2^1\ 1$

$$1\ 0\ 1 = 2^2 + 0 + 1 = 5$$
$$1\ 1\ 0 = 2^2 + 2^1 + 0 = 6$$
$$1\ 1\ 0\ 0 = 2^3 + 2^2 + 0 + 0 = 12$$
$$1\ 0\ 0\ 1\ 1 = 2^4 + 0 + 0 + 2^1 + 1 = 19$$
$$1\ 1\ 1\ 0\ 1 = 2^4 + 2^3 + 2^2 + 0 + 1 = 29$$
$$1\ 0\ 0\ 0\ 1\ 1 = 2^5 + 0 + 0 + 0 + 2^1 + 1 = 35$$

Factors and prime numbers

A number which divides exactly into another number is a factor of that number. Since 5 divides exactly into 30 six times, 5 and 6 are factors of 30; and since 2 divides exactly into 6 three times, 2 and 3 are factors of 6.

If a number has no factors and can only be divided by itself and by 1, it is called a prime number. Except for 2, all prime numbers are odd numbers.

Prime numbers from 1–1000

2	3	5	7	11	13	17	19	23	29
31	37	41	43	47	53	59	61	67	71
73	79	83	89	97	101	103	107	109	113
127	131	137	139	149	151	157	163	167	173
179	181	191	193	197	199	211	223	227	229
239	241	251	257	263	269	271	277	281	283
293	307	311	313	317	331	337	347	349	353
359	367	373	379	383	389	397	401	409	419
421	431	433	439	443	449	457	461	463	467
479	487	491	499	503	509	521	523	541	547
557	563	569	571	577	587	593	599	601	607
613	617	619	631	641	643	653	659	661	673
677	683	691	701	709	719	727	733	739	743
751	757	761	769	773	787	797	809	811	821
823	827	829	839	853	857	859	863	877	881
883	887	907	911	919	929	937	941	947	953
967	971	977	983	991	997				

Perfect numbers

Perfect numbers are whole numbers which are equal to the sum of all their factors excluding the number itself:

  6: the factors of 6 are 1, 2 and 3

    $1 + 2 + 3 = 6$

    ∴ 6 is a perfect number

28: the factors of 28 are 1, 2, 4, 7 and 14

    $1 + 2 + 4 + 7 + 14 = 28$

    ∴ 28 is a perfect number

These 2 perfect numbers were known to Pythagoras in the 6th century BC. The next 2 perfect numbers – 496 and 8128 – were discovered 300 years later by Nichomachus of Alexandria, who spent years searching for others. He failed to find them, but this is hardly surprising since the next one, recorded in a medieval manuscript, is 33,550,336. Until 1952, when a computer was used for the first time, only 7 more were found. Today we know of 30 perfect numbers.

The magic of 9

In the 9 times table, all digits in the answer add up to 9, e.g.:

    $6 \times 9 = 54 \ (5 + 4) = 9$

    $9 \times 9 = 81 \ (8 + 1) = 9$

    $91 \times 9 = 819 \ (8 + 1 + 9) = 18 \ (1 + 8) = 9$

    $32971 \times 9 = 296739 \ (2 + 9 + 6 + 7 + 3 + 9) = 36 \ (3 + 6) = 9$

Problems

59. Work out the sums in the progressive table below and see what the results are:

    $1 \times 9 + 2 =$

    $12 \times 9 + 3 =$

    $123 \times 9 + 4 =$

    $1234 \times 9 + 5 =$

    $12345 \times 9 + 6 =$

    $123456 \times 9 + 7 =$

    $1234567 \times 9 + 8 =$

    $12345678 \times 9 + 9 =$

60. Work out the sums in the progressive table below and see what the results are:

$$9 \times 9 + 7 =$$
$$98 \times 9 + 6 =$$
$$987 \times 9 + 5 =$$
$$9876 \times 9 + 4 =$$
$$98765 \times 9 + 3 =$$
$$987654 \times 9 + 2 =$$
$$9876543 \times 9 + 1 =$$
$$98765432 \times 9 + 0 =$$

61. Work out the sums in the progressive table below and see what the results are:

$$12345679 \times 9 \times 1 =$$
$$12345679 \times 9 \times 2 =$$
$$12345679 \times 9 \times 3 =$$
$$12345679 \times 9 \times 4 =$$
$$12345679 \times 9 \times 5 =$$
$$12345679 \times 9 \times 6 =$$
$$12345679 \times 9 \times 7 =$$
$$12345679 \times 9 \times 8 =$$
$$12345679 \times 9 \times 9 =$$

Differences in numbers exactly divisible by 9

If you rearrange the digits of any number in a different order and subtract the smaller from the larger, the difference between them will always be exactly divisible by 9:

321: the digits can be rearranged as 213 or 123

Number: 321 −
Rearranged: <u>213</u>
Subtracted: $108 \div 9 = 12$

Number: 321 −
Rearranged: <u>123</u>
Subtracted: $198 \div 9 = 22$

62841: the digits can be arranged in a number of ways, e.g.

86241 and 18624 (remember to subtract the smaller from the larger number):

Number:	86241 −
Rearranged:	<u>62841</u>
Subtracted:	23400 ÷ 9 = 2600

Number:	62841 −
Rearranged:	18624
Subtracted:	44217 ÷ 9 = 4913

Other progressive tables

62. Work out the sums in the progressive table below and see what the results are:

$37 \times 3 \times 1 =$
$37 \times 3 \times 2 =$
$37 \times 3 \times 3 =$
$37 \times 3 \times 4 =$
$37 \times 3 \times 5 =$
$37 \times 3 \times 6 =$
$37 \times 3 \times 7 =$
$37 \times 3 \times 8 =$
$37 \times 3 \times 9 =$

63. Write down and continue the progressive table below and see what the results are:

$15873 \times 7 \times 1 =$
$15873 \times 7 \times 2 =$
$15873 \times 7 \times 3 =$
$15873 \times 7 \times 4 =$
$15873 \times 7 \times 5 =$
$15873 \times 7 \times 6 =$
$15873 \times 7 \times 7 =$
$15873 \times 7 \times 8 =$
$15873 \times 7 \times 9 =$

Repeating patterns

● If you continue the sequence below, you will see that the result is a repeating pattern:

$101 \times 12 = 1212$
$10101 \times 12 = 121212$
$1010101 \times 12 = 12121212$

• You can produce similar patterns if you multiply 101, 10101, 1010101 etc. by any two-digit numbers:

$101 \times 27 = 2727$
$10101 \times 94 = 949494$
$1010101 \times 88 = 88888888$

• If you place an extra nought between the ones of the number being multiplied, you can multiply by any three-digit number and obtain a similar pattern:

$1001 \times 234 = 234234$
$1001001 \times 378 = 378378378$

• If you increase the number of noughts between the ones, you can multiply by numbers with many more digits and produce repeating patterns. Remember that the same number of noughts must be repeated between each one, and that the number you are multiplying by must always have one more digit than the number of noughts:

$10001 \times 1925 = 19251925$
$100010001 \times 1925 = 192519251925$
$1000010000100001 \times 61253 = 61253612536125361253$

64. If you complete this mirror-image sum, you will find that there is a repeating pattern in the answer.

```
1 2 3 4 5 6 7 8 9  +    9 8 7 6 5 4 3 2 1   +
1 2 3 4 5 6 7 8          8 7 6 5 4 3 2 1
1 2 3 4 5 6 7              7 6 5 4 3 2 1
1 2 3 4 5 6                  6 5 4 3 2 1
1 2 3 4 5                      5 4 3 2 1
1 2 3 4                          4 3 2 1
1 2 3                              3 2 1
1 2                                  2 1
1                                      1
———————————————      ———————————————


———————————————      ———————————————
```

Quick conversions

There are times when it's useful to be able to make a quick conversion from Imperial measurement to metric or the other way round. Some methods of doing this are given below, but you should realise that these will only give you a rough and ready guide.

The examples which are given below show the difference between the correct answer and the result of making the quick conversion. Note that the higher the number you are converting, the greater the discrepancy in the answer.

Examples of quick conversions

Imperial	How to convert to metric
• feet to metres	multiply by 3, divide by 10, e.g.
19 feet	$19 \times 3 = 57 \div 10 =$
quick answer:	5.7
answer:	5.8192
• yards to metres	subtract $\frac{1}{10}$
21 yards	$\frac{1}{10}$ of $21 = 2.1$
	$21 - 2.1 =$
quick answer:	18.9
answer:	19.202
• miles to kilometres (1)	divide by 5, multiply by 8
40 miles	$40 \div 5 = 8$
	$8 \times 8 =$
quick answer:	64
answer:	64.36
• miles to kilometres (2)	add $\frac{3}{5}$
40 miles	$\frac{3}{5}$ of $40 =$
	$24 + 40 =$
quick answer:	64
answer:	64.36

- sq yards to sq metres subtract $\frac{1}{6}$
   30 sq yards $\frac{1}{6}$ of 30 =
            30 − 5 =
  quick answer: 25
    answer: 25.08

- sq miles to sq kilometres multiply × $2\frac{3}{5}$
   25 sq miles $25 \times \frac{13}{5} =$
  quick answer: 65
    answer: 64.85

cu yards to cu metres subtract $\frac{1}{4}$
   80 cu yards $\frac{1}{4}$ of 80 = 20
            80 − 20 =
  quick answer: 60
    answer: 61.12

- lbs to kilograms subtract $\frac{1}{10}$, divide by 2
     5 lbs $\frac{1}{10}$ of 5 = $\frac{1}{2}$, $5 - \frac{1}{2} =$
            $4\frac{1}{2} \div 2 =$
            $2\frac{1}{4} =$
  quick answer: 2.25
    answer: 2.265

- sq metres to sq yards add $\frac{1}{5}$
   55 sq metres $\frac{1}{5}$ of 55 =
            11 + 55 =
  quick answer: 66
    answer: 65.725

- cu metres to cu yards add $\frac{1}{3}$
   21 cu metres $\frac{1}{3}$ of 21 =
            7 + 21 =
  quick answer: 28
    answer: 27.477

- kilograms to lbs add $\frac{1}{10}$, multiply by 2
   40 kilograms $\frac{1}{10}$ of 40 =
            4 + 40 = 44 × 2 =
  quick answer: 88
    answer: 88.16

- litres to pints   add $\frac{3}{4}$

     28 litres $\frac{3}{4}$ of 28 =

                21 + 28 =

     quick answer: 49

     answer: 49.252

- pints to litres   multiply by 3, divide by 5

     15 pints   15 × 3 =

             45 ÷ 5 =

     quick answer: 9

     answer: 8.79

Metric   **How to convert to Imperial**

- metres to feet   multiply by 13, divide by 4

     60 metres   60 × 13 =

             780 ÷ 4 =

     quick answer: 195

     answer: 196.8

- kilometres to miles   multiply by 5, divide by 8

     32 kilometres   32 × 5 =

             160 ÷ 8 =

     quick answer: 20

     answer: 19.872

- sq kilometres to sq miles   multiply by 2, divide by 5

     61 sq kilometres   61 × 2 =

             122 ÷ 5 =

     quick answer: 24.4

     answer: 23.546

Problems

Using the quick method of conversion, see if you can change:

65. 35 miles to kilometres.
66. 30 lbs to kilograms.
67. 56 litres to pints.
68. 76 sq metres to sq yards.
69. 24 kilometres to miles.

70. 7 metres to feet.
71. 29 yards to metres.
72. 25 lbs to kilograms.
73. 20 sq miles to sq kilometres.

Magic squares

Magic squares are sets of figures written in a square in which each horizontal row, vertical column and major diagonal all add up to the same number.

● They are thought to have been devised in India about 2,000 years ago and were introduced into Europe in the 15th century. People then were very superstitious, and because it was believed that they would keep away the plague, some wealthy people had magic squares engraved on silver plates.

Examples of magic squares

4	3	8
9	5	1
2	7	6

Horizontal: $4 + 3 + 8 = 15$
$9 + 5 + 1 = 15$
$2 + 7 + 6 = 15$
Vertical: $4 + 9 + 2 = 15$
$3 + 5 + 7 = 15$
$8 + 1 + 6 = 15$
Diagonal: $4 + 5 + 6 = 15$
$8 + 5 + 2 = 15$

16	3	2	13
5	10	11	8
9	6	7	12
4	15	14	1

Horizontal $16 + 3 + 2 + 13 = 34$
$5 + 10 + 11 + 8 = 34$
$9 + 6 + 7 + 12 = 34$
$4 + 15 + 14 + 1 = 34$
Vertical: $16 + 5 + 9 + 4 = 34$
$3 + 10 + 6 + 15 = 34$
$2 + 11 + 7 + 14 = 34$
$13 + 8 + 12 + 1 = 34$
Diagonal: $16 + 10 + 7 + 1 = 34$
$13 + 11 + 6 + 4 = 34$

In this case, 4 squares of figures also add up to 34

Squares:
$$16 + 3 + 5 + 10 = 34$$
$$2 + 13 + 11 + 8 = 34$$
$$9 + 6 + 4 + 15 = 34$$
$$7 + 12 + 14 + 1 = 34$$

Problems

Magic squares to complete

74.

8	1	6
3		7
4	9	

75.

2	7	
9		1
4	3	8

76.

6	1	
	5	3
2		4

77.

14	3	4	17
	12	11	6
13		7	
2			

78.

17		3	14
	11	12	
10	7		
5			2

Plane shapes

Plane shapes are two dimensional (i.e. flat) and there are several kinds, e.g. circles, rectangles, squares and triangles. All of these, except the circles, are polygons.

● Polygon comes from the Greek *poly* meaning 'many' and *gonia* meaning 'angled'.

● Polygons can be regular, with all sides and angles equal, or irregular, with sides of different lengths and angles of different sizes.

Polygons

Name	Number of sides	Internal angle	Sum of internal angles
equilateral triangles	3	60°	180°
square	4	90°	360°
pentagon	5	108°	540°
hexagon	6	120°	720°
heptagon	7	128.6°	900.2°
octagon	8	135°	1080°
nonagon	9	140°	1260°
decagon	10	147.3°	1473°
dodecagon	12	150°	1800°

Formulae for use with plane shapes

Abbreviations

a = length of top
b = length of base
d = length of diameter
h = perpendicular height
r = length of radius
pi = π, the ratio of the circumference of a circle to its diameter. Its value is approximated as 3.1416 or $\frac{22}{7}$.

Area

Type	Formula
circle	πr^2
cylinder, curved surface	$2\pi rh$
cylinder, total surface area	$2\pi r(h + r)$
parallelogram	bh
rectangle	ab
rectangular block, surface area	$2(ab + bh + ha)$
rhombus	$\frac{1}{2}$ product of the diagonals
sphere, surface area	$4\pi r^2$
square	a^2
trapezium	$\frac{1}{2}(a + b)h$
triangle	$\frac{1}{2}bh$

Volume

Type	Formula
cone	$\frac{1}{3}\pi r^2 h$
cylinder, closed	$\pi r^2 h$
pyramid, rectangular base	$\frac{1}{3}(ab)h$
sphere	$\frac{4}{3}\pi r^3$

Perimeter of plane shapes

Type	Formula
circle, circumference	$2\pi r$ or πd
parallelogram	$2(a + b)$
rectangle	$2(a + b)$
rhombus	$4a$
square	$4a$

Polyhedrons

Solid figures are three-dimensional: they have length, width and depth.
● Regular polyhedrons have faces consisting of identical regular polygons. Semi-regular polyhedrons have faces consisting of two or more different types of polygons.

Regular polyhedrons

Name	Number of faces	Type of face
tetrahedron	4	triangular
cube	6	square
octahedron	8	triangular
dodecahedron	12	five sided
icosahedron	20	triangular

Semi-regular polyhedrons

Name	Number of faces	Type of face
cuboctahedron	14	square, triangular
octahedron, truncated	14	hexagonal, square
cuboctahedron, truncated	26	hexagonal, octagonal, square
icosidodecahedron	32	pentagonal, triangular
icosahedron, truncated	32	hexagonal, pentagonal
icosidodecahedron, truncated	62	pentagonal, square, decagonal

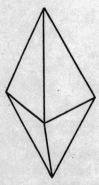

Octahedron

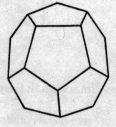

Dodecahedron

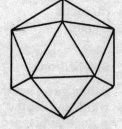

Icosahedron

Answers to problems

1. $19 \times 99 = 1,881$
2. $13 \times 297 = 3,861$
3. $52 \times 496 = 25,792$
4. $24 \times 11 = 264$
5. $63 \times 11 = 693$
6. $55 \times 11 = 605$
7. $84 \times 11 = 924$
8. $96 \times 11 = 1,056$
9. $523 \times 11 = 5,753$
10. $614 \times 11 = 6,754$
11. $274 \times 11 = 3,014$
12. $12,356 \times 11 = 135,916$
13. $2,312 \times 12 = 27,744$
14. $5,412 \times 12 = 64,944$
15. $17,486 \times 12 = 209,832$
16. $53 \times 25 = 1,325$
17. $94 \times 36 = 3,384$
18. $82 \times 24 = 1,968$
19. $295 \div 10 = 29.5$
20. $4614 \div 100 = 46.14$
21. $928,756 \div 100,000 = 9.28756$
22. $728 \div 10,000 = 0.0728$
23. $9 \div 1,000 = 0.009$
24. No
25. No
26. Yes
27. No
28. Yes
29. Yes
30. No
31. Yes
32. Yes
33. Yes
34. No
35. Yes
36. No
37. Yes
38. Yes

39. $69,714 \div 15 = \mathbf{4{,}647}$ remainder **9**
40. $45,674 \div 21 = \mathbf{2{,}174}$ remainder **20**
41. $69,253 \div 42 = \mathbf{1{,}648}$ remainder **37**
42. $576,284 \div 49 = \mathbf{11{,}760}$ remainder **44**
43. $524 \div 99 = \mathbf{5}$ remainder **29**
44. $683 \div 99 = \mathbf{6}$ remainder **89**
45. $748 \div 99 = \mathbf{7}$ remainder **55**
46. $1,240 \div 99 = \mathbf{12}$ remainder **52**
47. $621 \div 98 = \mathbf{6}$ remainder **33**
48. $809 \div 98 = \mathbf{8}$ remainder **25**
49. $1,421 \div 98 = \mathbf{14}$ remainder **49**
50. $410 \div 95 = \mathbf{4}$ remainder **30**
51. $716 \div 96 = \mathbf{7}$ remainder **44**
52. $631 \div 97 = \mathbf{6}$ remainder **49**
53. $23 \times 22 = \mathbf{506}$
54. $19 \times 23 = \mathbf{437}$
55. $23 \times 24 = \mathbf{552}$
56. $418 \div 19 = \mathbf{22}$
57. $463 \div 22 = \mathbf{21}$ remainder **1**
58. $287 \div 19 = \mathbf{15}$ remainder **2**
59.
```
        11
       111
      1111
     11111
    111111
   1111111
  11111111
 111111111
```
60.
```
        88
       888
      8888
     88888
    888888
   8888888
  88888888
 888888888
```

61. 111111111
222222222
333333333
444444444
555555555
666666666
777777777
888888888
999999999

62. 111
222
333
444
555
666
777
888
999

63. 111111
222222
333333
444444
555555
666666
777777
888888
999999

64. 1083676269, 1083676269
65. 35 miles = 56 kilometres
66. 30 lbs = 13.5 kilograms
67. 56 litres = 98 pints
68. 76 sq metres = 91.2 sq yards
69. 24 kilometres = 15 miles
70. 7 metres = 22.75 feet
71. 29 yards = 26.1 metres
72. 25 lbs = 11.25 kilograms

73. 20 sq miles = 52 sq kilometres

74.

8	1	6
3	5	7
4	9	2

75.

2	7	6
9	5	1
4	3	8

76.

6	1	8
7	5	3
2	9	4

77.

14	3	4	17
9	12	11	6
13	8	7	10
2	15	16	5

78.

17	4	3	14
6	11	12	9
10	7	8	13
5	16	15	2

116

8 | LUCKY AND UNLUCKY NUMBERS

Numbers have always been thought to have a special significance, but what is lucky for one is unlucky for others. Colours are associated with some numbers, but these run out after 7. Some numbers are represented by signs of the Zodiac, but after the number 9 these either disappear altogether or are not agreed upon by various authorities. Other numbers have very little symbolic meaning.

However, numbers do appear in rhymes all over the world; this is typical:

> *Seven blackbirds in a tree,*
> *Count them and see what they be.*
> *One for sorrow, two for joy,*
> *Three for a girl and four for a boy,*
> *Five for silver, six for gold,*
> *Seven for a secret that's never been told.*

Number 1

The Chinese and the Greeks thought that the number 1 was both an odd and even number which represented unity and reason. To the Chinese, it was a number that symbolised the sky. Its colour is red and it is represented by Aries the Ram. To see a single magpie or blackbird is considered unlucky; if you should spot one, you must immediately look for another to wipe out the misfortune.

Number 2

Once again the Chinese and the Greeks thought this a female number, and since it was the first female number it was particularly fortunate. The Greeks believed that all even numbers were female and all odd numbers except 1 were male. The number 2, although important, also represented those who couldn't make up their minds – that is, they were in two minds. To the Chinese, it symbolised the earth. It is represented by Taurus the Bull and its colour is orange. To see pairs of birds is good luck, and of course 2 is company, but 3 is none.

Gorgon (see over)

118

Number 3

3 was important to the Greeks because it was the first male number and symbolised strength. It was magical as well, since it represented the beginning, the middle and the end of life and because the world was divided into heaven, the earth and the underworld. It was significant to Christians. God is the Trinity. He is God the Father, God the Son and God the Holy Ghost. Oddly enough, there were trinities of gods in Ancient Egypt and in Babylon. To the Chinese it symbolised fire, and its colour is yellow. It is represented by Gemini the Twins.

3 occurs over and over again in folklore throughout the world. Oaths and charms are repeated 3 times. Good luck comes in threes, and so does bad luck. When you see the new moon you should bow or curtsey 3 times and money, preferably silver, should be turned over 3 times in your pocket – that will help it to multiply.

In Greek mythology there were:

3 Fates: three goddesses who controlled human destiny.

3 Furies: three women with snakes coiled in their hair who punished those who committed crimes which had not been avenged.

3 Gorgons: three sisters, also with snakes in their hair. They looked so frightful that anyone who saw them immediately turned to stone.

Number 4

The Greeks thought that the number 4 represented harmony and justice because it is a number divided into 2 parts. This made it lucky, as did the fact that there are the 4 elements: earth, air, fire and water. It symbolised water to the Chinese; its colour is green and it is represented by Cancer the Crab.

In medieval times people thought that there were four humours which influenced man's temperament and health. These were fluids in the body – blood, phlegm, yellow bile and black bile. Blood was the only one worth having. It meant that you were comparatively good-humoured and optimistic. Phlegm indicated that you were sluggish and dull. Yellow bile or choler meant you were an angry or irritable person, while melancholy was the result of black bile.

Number 5

This number represented marriage to the Greeks since 2 (female number) + 3 (male number) = 5. In addition it held the secret of colour. It symbolised air to the Chinese; its colour is blue and it is represented by Leo the Lion. Many consider it an unlucky number because magicians and witches used a pentacle, a 5-pointed star. It was also thought unlucky since 5 wounds were inflicted on Christ during the crucifixion.

Number 6

This is the first perfect number (*see* Perfect Numbers) and was therefore an important number and a lucky one to the Greeks. It represented man, since we have 2 arms, 2 legs, a trunk and a head. It is also significant because God created the world in 6 days. It symbolised the wind to the Chinese; its colour is blue and it is represented by Virgo the Virgin.

Number 7

7 was an important number in the ancient world. The 7 known planets were though to govern the universe, there were 7 days in the week and 7 colours in the rainbow. The 7th child in a family is still often thought to have special gifts, while the 7th child of a 7th child is believed to have second sight. 7 was the number which held the secret of health; its colour is violet and it is represented by Libra the scales. To the Chinese, it symbolised a mountain.

In many countries it is believed that 7 horseshoes nailed above or on a door prevents evil from entering the building.

Number 8

The Greeks thought that 8 represented wisdom, and it was also believed to signify magic and science. Its colour is pink and it is represented by Scorpio the Scorpion.

Number 9

To the Greeks this was a number with special
powers, e.g. $2 \times 9 = 18 = (1 + 8) = 9$, and the numbers
1–9 make a magic square (*see* Mathematical
Oddities, Magic Squares). It held the secret of
healing, but it has no colour – as have none of the
higher numbers – since the colours of the rainbow
have been used up. It is represented by Sagittarius.

This is another number which occurs in folklore.
It is said that warts will disappear if you look up at
the full moon and then blow on them 9 times.

In Greek mythology there are 9 Muses: the
goddesses Clio, Calliope, Euterpe, Erato,
Melpomene, Polyhymnia, Terpsichore, Thalia and
Urania, who presided over literature, music, the
arts and sciences.

Numbers 10 and 11

There is very little of significance about these
numbers. 10s are important because we count in
10s. Had man been born with only 4 fingers on each
hand, we should probably be counting in eights. 10s
occur in rhymes and songs because it is a way of
teaching children to count.

● 11 is only interesting from a mathematical point
of view (*see* Quick Methods of Multiplying and
Dividing). It was used in the Imperial method of
measuring length; e.g. half of 11 was a rod, pole or
perch; a mile, or 1,760 yards is 11×160, and
22 yards make a chain.

Number 12

12 was always considered an important number. There are 12 months in the year, 2 times 12 hours in a day, and 12 signs of the Zodiac. It was thought by many to be lucky. Perhaps that is because of 'And twelve for the twelve apostles' — a line in the old song 'Green Grow the Rushes-O'.

Number 13

Although there are a few who believe 13 a lucky number, most people do not. There is a special word to describe those who have a real dread of it: *triskaidekaphobia*. In some countries the number never appears in house numbering but 14 follows 12; this is also true of the numbering of rooms in many hotels.

13 is almost certainly thought unlucky because of the Last Supper, when there were 12 disciples and Jesus present. The unluckiest day of all is Friday the 13th, since Christ was crucified on a Friday.

9 | NUMBERS AT HOME

Cooking and shopping

Today everyone seems to have a large number of electrical gadgets. These should make life simpler, but so often it becomes more complicated since there is so much more to go wrong.

Even in the kitchen there are complications. Lots of people like using foreign recipes, but it can be infuriating to find that the measurements in a recipe book are metric, or that the oven temperature is given in degrees centigrade when you are using a gas oven.

Oven temperatures

C°	F°	Gas mark	Heat level
110	225	$\frac{1}{4}$	very cool
120	230	$\frac{1}{2}$	very cool
140	275	1	cool
150	300	2	cool
160	325	3	moderate
180	350	4	moderate
190	375	5	moderately hot
200	400	6	moderately hot
220	425	7	hot
230	450	8	hot
240	475	9	very hot

Dry weight

The measurements given below are not exact since these would result in awkward quantities. It's simpler to use the recommended weights listed; although they are not precisely accurate conversions, they should give satisfactory results.

Ounces	Recommended (grams)	Approximate metric (grams)
1	25	28
2	50	57
3	75	85
4 ($\frac{1}{4}$lb)	100	113
5	150	142
6	175	170
7	200	198
8 ($\frac{1}{2}$lb)	225	227
9	250	255
10	275	283
11	300	312
12 ($\frac{3}{4}$lb)	350	340
13	375	368
14	400	396
15	425	425
16 (1 lb)	450	454

Liquid measurement

Quantity	Recommended (ml)	Approximate metric (ml)
2 fl ozs	55	56.2
$\frac{1}{4}$ pint	150	142
$\frac{1}{2}$ pint	300	283
$\frac{3}{4}$ pint	450	425
1 pint	600	567
1$\frac{1}{2}$ pint	900	851
1$\frac{3}{4}$ pint	1000 (1 litre)	992

Capacity

Very often measurements in recipes are given in cups, teaspoons and tablespoons. An approximate guide to these is given below.

Measurement	Imperial	Metric
1 small teaspoon	$\frac{1}{8}$ fl oz	3.5 ml
1 standard teaspoon	$\frac{1}{6}$ fl oz	4.74 ml
1 tablespoon	$\frac{1}{2}$ fl oz	14.2 ml (0.0142 l)
1 tea cup	8 fl oz	0.2272 l
1 breakfast cup	10 fl oz	0.2841 l

Measuring cups

1 standard measuring cup (UK) = 10 fl oz
1 standard measuring cup (USA) = 8 fl oz
Converting the measurement of dry ingredients when using measuring cups is not easy. This is because the weight of dry ingredients varies according to their density:

USA cups	UK (oz)
1 cup butter	8
1 cup flour	4
1 cup rice	8
1 cup sugar, brown	$6\frac{1}{2}$
1 cup sugar, white	8

Tablespoons

The size of tablespoons also varies:

Country	Metric (ml)
Australia	20
UK	17.7
USA	14.2

Comparison of prices in pounds and kilograms

Price per kg	Price per lb
2.2 pence	1 pence
4.4 pence	2 pence
6.6 pence	3 pence

8.8 pence	4 pence
11 pence	5 pence
13.2 pence	6 pence
15.4 pence	7 pence
17.6 pence	8 pence
19.8 pence	9 pence
22 pence	10 pence
24.2 pence	11 pence
26.4 pence	12 pence
28.6 pence	13 pence
30.8 pence	14 pence
33 pence	15 pence
35.2 pence	16 pence
37.4 pence	17 pence
39.6 pence	18 pence
41.8 pence	19 pence
44 pence	20 pence
46.2 pence	21 pence
48.4 pence	22 pence
50.6 pence	23 pence
52.8 pence	24 pence
55.0 pence	25 pence
57.2 pence	26 pence
59.4 pence	27 pence
61.6 pence	28 pence
63.8 pence	29 pence
66.0 pence	30 pence
68.2 pence	31 pence
70.4 pence	32 pence
72.6 pence	33 pence
74.8 pence	34 pence
77.0 pence	35 pence
79.2 pence	36 pence
81.4 pence	37 pence
83.6 pence	38 pence
85.8 pence	39 pence
88 pence	40 pence
90.2 pence	41 pence
92.4 pence	42 pence

94.6 pence	43 pence
96.8 pence	44 pence
99.0 pence	45 pence
101.2 pence	46 pence
103.4 pence	47 pence
105.6 pence	48 pence
107.8 pence	49 pence
110 pence	50 pence

Clothing sizes

Clothes are sized in various ways throughout the world –
there is no universal international standard. There are
even variations within the same country, so the following
list should be used as a guide only. *Note:* most European
countries use centimetres instead of a size number.

Conversions

Women's blouses, coats, dresses and jackets

Most of Europe	76 cm	81 cm	86 cm	91 cm	97 cm	102 cm
Japan	7	9	11	13	15	17
Scandinavia	36	38	40	42	44	46
Spain	40	42	44	46	48	50
UK	10	12	14	16	18	20
USA	8	10	12	14	16	18

Women's shoes

Most of Europe, Middle East	36	37	38	39	40	41
Japan	22	23	24	25	26	
UK	3	4	5	6	7	8
USA	$4\frac{1}{2}$	$5\frac{1}{2}$	$6\frac{1}{2}$	$7\frac{1}{2}$	$8\frac{1}{2}$	$9\frac{1}{2}$

Men's suits, overcoats

Almost universal	46	48	50	54	56	58

Men's shirts

Most of Europe, Middle East	36	37	38	39	40	41	42
UK	14	$14\frac{1}{2}$	15	$15\frac{1}{2}$	16	$16\frac{1}{2}$	17
USA	14	$14\frac{1}{2}$	15	$15\frac{1}{2}$	16	$16\frac{1}{2}$	17

Men's shoes

Most of Europe, Middle East	39	40	41	42	43	44	45
Scandinavia	40	41	42	43	44	45	46
UK	6	7	8	9	10	11	12
USA	$6\frac{1}{2}$	$7\frac{1}{2}$	$8\frac{1}{2}$	$9\frac{1}{2}$	$10\frac{1}{2}$	$11\frac{1}{2}$	$12\frac{1}{2}$

Dress pattern sizes

Size	Bust		Waist		Hips	
	ins	cm	ins	cm	ins	cm
10	$32\frac{1}{2}$	83	25	64	$34\frac{1}{2}$	88
12	34	87	$26\frac{1}{2}$	67	36	92
14	36	92	28	71	38	97
16	38	97	30	76	40	102
18	40	102	32	81	42	107

Note: all dress pattern sizes are usually based on actual body measurement and not on the finished size of the garment.

Fabric widths

ins	cm
35/36	90
44/45	115
48	120
54/56	140
60	150
90	225

Conversion

To convert inches to millimetres, multiply by 25.4.
To convert inches to centimetres, multiply by 2.54.
To convert feet to metres, multiply by 0.3048.
To convert yards to metres, multiply by 0.9144.

Diet

People usually go on a diet because they don't want to be
fat. They cut out bread and cakes or munch apples instead
of chocolates, but many of them forget that they won't be
healthy even if they are thin unless they have a balanced
diet. While a calorie table might be helpful when deciding
whether to have eggs and bacon or grapefruit for breakfast,
other factors such as the protein, vitamin, mineral, starch
and sugar content also need to be taken into account.

Calories

What you have to remember is that everything we do – and
that includes sleeping – uses energy, and this energy has to
be replaced. Once consumed, food supplies this need.
● We use the word calorie, but energy is actually measured
in kilocalories (kcal) and, increasingly, in kilojoules (kJ).
● The amount of calories that a person needs varies from
one individual to another. Someone doing heavy manual
work requires more than someone who is stuck at a desk
all day, and a pregnant woman needs more than a woman
doing an ordinary day's housework.
● If you spend all day in bed, you are only using up about
60 calories an hour, but if you go for a walk and stride for
about four miles in an hour, you will have used up over 490
calories.
● A reasonably active woman weighing approximately $8\frac{1}{2}$
stone (55 kg), needs something like 2,300 calories a day.
A man who is reasonably fit and active and weighs about
$10\frac{1}{4}$ stone (65 kg) needs about 3,200 calories.
● The calorific value of the foods listed below is only
intended as a rough guide. Although the value for raw

apples is given in ounces, for example, it's most unlikely that you will weigh one before eating it and anyway, some apples are sweeter than others. The way in which things are cooked varies too; an apple pie baked by one person will differ from that baked by another.

● In the table below, the number of calories is given for both 1 oz and 100 grams. Kilojoule values are stated as well.

	Calories		Kilojoules
	1 oz	100 g	
Cereals and pasta			
bread, white	70	247	937
bread, wholemeal	61	216	907
cornflakes	101	354	1486
muesli	103	363	1524
rice	35	123	517
spaghetti	34	120	504
Dairy products			
butter	210	740	3084
cheese, Cheddar	114	403	1692
cream, double	127	450	1890
egg, boiled	41	146	612
ice cream	47	166	697
margarine	206	730	3057
milk, liquid	18	66	274
yoghurt	60	215	903
Fish			
cod, fried in batter	56	198	732
haddock, boiled	22	79	317
herring, grilled	38	153	743
prawns	30	106	504
salmon, poached	40	142	596
sardines, tinned	58	205	861

Fruit (uncooked)

apple	12	47	199
banana	22	78	328
grapefruit	11	40	168
lemon	4	15	63
orange	10	35	147
peach	11	39	164
pear	8	30	126
pear, avocado	62	223	937
strawberry	7	23	168

Cakes and puddings

apple pie	79	280	1179
chocolate cake	112	396	1663
Christmas pudding	92	325	1365
currant bun	93	329	1385
doughnut, cream and jam	100	353	1482
jelly	16	56	237
lemon meringue pie	55	194	815
rice pudding	44	141	594
trifle	50	177	741

Meat

beef, lean roast	60	212	890
chicken, roast	44	155	651
lamb chop, grilled	78	277	1163
liver, fried lamb's	66	233	959
pork, roast	81	286	1201
sausage, grilled pork	90	317	1902
turkey, roast	40	140	588

Vegetables

beans, baked	26	90	378
beans, runner, boiled	2	7	29
carrots, boiled	15	52	218
celery, uncooked	3	10	42
lettuce, raw	4	12	50
potatoes, boiled	22	78	328
potato chips, fried	75	265	1113
tomato, uncooked	4	12	50

Miscellaneous

chocolate, milk	150	530	2226
chocolate, plain	148	522	2192
coleslaw	36	126	529
fish pie, potato-topped	37	132	554
pâté, fish	70	247	1037
pâté, meat	85	300	1260
peanuts, roast salted	154	544	2284
potato crisps	150	529	2221
potato salad	34	155	651
shepherd's pie	32	112	470
Yorkshire pudding	60	212	890

Conversion of ounces and grams

To convert 1 ounce to 100 grams, multiply by 3.53.
To convert 100 grams to 1 ounce divide by 3.53.
Note: figures in the table have been rounded up or down to
the nearest whole number. 4.2 has been used for the
conversion of kilojoules to calories.

Radio

Radio used to be known as 'the wireless'. This was because
it transmits electrical signals without the use of wires,
sound being converted into electromagnetic waves. These
electromagnetic waves are transmitted into a receiver, and
then converted back into sound.
● Originally radio stations were recognised by
wavelengths which were measured in metres, but today
frequencies are measured in kilohertz (kHz) or megahertz
(MHz). The SI unit for frequency is hertz (Hz).

    1000 Hz = 1 kHz
    1000 kHz = 1 MHz

Some wavelengths and frequencies

Wavelength	Frequency
5 mm	60,000 MHz
1 cm	30,000 MHz
5 cm	6,000 MHz
10 cm	3,000 MHz

1 m	300 MHz
3 m	100 MHz
5 m	60 MHz
50 m	6 MHz
100 m	3,000 kHz
200 m	1,500 kHz
300 m	1,000 kHz
500 m	600 kHz
1,000 m	300 kHz
2,000 m	150 kHz

Radio bands

Abbreviation		Frequency
VLF	very low frequency	below 30 kHz
LF	low frequency	30–300 kHz
MF	medium frequency	300–3,000 kHz
HF	high frequency	3,000–30,000 kHz
VHF	very high frequency	30–300 MHz
UHF	ultra high frequency	300–3,000 MHz
SHF	super high frequency	3,000–30,000 MHz
EHF	extremely high frequency	30,000–300,000 MHz

BBC radio wavelengths

Station	kHz	MHz	m
Radio 1	1053		285
	1089		275
	VHF	88–90.2	
Radio 2	693		433
	909		330
	VHF	88–90.2	
Radio 3	125		247
	VHF	90–92.5	
Radio 4	200		1500
	VHF	92–95	
Radio Cymru	VHF	92–95	
Radio Scotland	810		370
	VHF	92–95	
Radio Wales	882		340
Radio Ulster	1341		234
	VHF	92–95	

10 | NUMBERS IN SPORT

Olympic Games

The original Olympic Games were held once every four years at Olympia in Greece. The earliest ever recorded took place in 776 BC, but we know that they were staged long before that. They were abandoned in AD 393.

In the late nineteenth century a Frenchman, Baron de Courbertin, managed to interest a small number of sportsmen in the idea of reviving the games, and the first modern Olympics were held in 1896 in Athens. They have taken place every 4 years since then, except for the periods during the 2 World Wars. Even so, those which had already been planned but did not in fact take place are included in the numbering of the games.

Number	Date	City	Country	Countries Participating
I	1896	Athens	Greece	13
II	1900	Paris	France	22
III	1904	St Louis	USA	13
IV	1908	London	UK	22
V	1912	Stockholm	Sweden	28
VI	1916	Berlin	Germany	—
VII	1920	Antwerp	Belgium	29
VIII	1924	Paris	France	44
IX	1928	Amsterdam	Holland	46
X	1932	Los Angeles	USA	37
XI	1936	Berlin	Germany	49
XII	1940	Tokyo	Japan	—
XIII	1944	London	UK	—
XIV	1948	London	UK	59
XV	1952	Helsinki	Finland	69
XVI	1956	Melbourne	Australia	67
XVII	1960	Rome	Italy	83
XVIII	1964	Tokyo	Japan	93
XIX	1968	Mexico City	Mexico	112
XX	1972	Munich	FRG (West Germany)	122
XXI	1976	Montreal	Canada	92
XXII	1980	Moscow	USSR	81

XXIII	1984	Los Angeles	USA	140
XXIV	1988	Seoul	South Korea	160
XXV	1992	Barcelona	Spain	

Winter Olympic Games

Although Winter Olympic Games were held during the 1908 and 1920 Olympics in London and Antwerp, it wasn't until 1924 that they took place in a different venue. As a result, the numbering of the Winter Olympics dates from that event.

Number	Date	City	Country	Countries participating
I	1924	Chamonix	France	16
II	1928	St Moritz	Switzerland	25
III	1932	Lake Placid	USA	17
IV	1936	Garmisch-Partenkirchen	Germany	28
V	1948	St Moritz	Switzerland	28
VI	1952	Oslo	Norway	22
VII	1956	Cortina d'Ampezzo	Italy	32
VIII	1960	Squaw Valley	USA	30
IX	1964	Innsbruck	Austria	36
X	1968	Grenoble	France	37
XI	1972	Sapporo	Japan	35
XII	1976	Innsbruck	Austria	37
XIII	1980	Lake Placid	USA	37
XIV	1984	Sarajevo	Yugoslavia	49
XV	1988	Calgary	Canada	49
XVI	1992	St Moritz	France	

Sport

Archery

There are various forms that this sport takes. Many people enjoy target or field archery, where points are scored on a target, as well as distance shooting.

Target shooting	Statistics
distance from target	: 30m, 50m, 70m, 90m with 36 arrows shot from each mark

scoring, international (zones divided into 2)	: white 1 or 2 points, black 3 or 4 points, blue 5 or 6 points, red 7 or 8 points, yellow 9 or 10 points
scoring, British (5-zone target)	: white 1 point, black 3 points, blue 5 points, red 7 points, yellow 9 points

Athletics

The events listed below are those which are included in the Olympic Games, but there are many others in which athletes participate.

Running	Statistics
sprints	: 100m, 200m, 400m
middle distance	: 800m, 1500m, 3000m (women only)
long distance	: 5000m, 10000m
marathon	: 42.195 km (26 miles 385 yds)
relays	: 4 × 100 m, 4 × 400 m
steeplechase (28 hurdles, 7 water jumps)	: 3000 m (men only)
hurdling	: 100 m (women only), 110 m (men only), 400 m

Walking	: 20 km, 50 km

Combined events

decathlon (10 events) (men only)	: Day One: 100 m, long jump, shot putt, high jump, 400 m
	: Day Two: 110 m hurdles, discus, pole vault, javelin, 1500 m
heptathlon (7 events) (women only)	: Day One: 100 m, 100 m hurdles, high jump, shot putt, 200 m
	: Day Two: long jump, javelin, 800 m

modern pentathlon (5 events)	: cross-country riding 5000 m, fencing, shooting, swimming 300m, cross-country running (men only) 4000 m

Field events	**Statistics**
discus	: weight 2 kg (men), 1 kg (women) : diameter 220 mm (men), 180 mm (women)
hammer	: weight 7.26 kg, overall length 1.19 m (men only)
high jump	: width between uprights 3.66–4.04m, 3 failures at any one height results in elimination, take-off on one foot only
javelin	: weight 800 g (men), 600 g (women) : length 2.7 m (men), 2.3 m (women)

long jump	: 3 jumps with distance measured from take-off board to nearest mark to it made by competitor; leading 8 competitors allowed 3 more jumps
pole vault	: uprights 3.66–4.37 m apart, flexible pole placed in 1 m long box; lower hand must not be raised above upper hand during jump (men only)
shot putt	: weight 7.26 kg (men), 4 kg (women)

triple jump	: take-off on one foot, landing on same foot; step on to second foot; jump completed as for long jump

Badminton

Statistics

number of players	: 2 or 4
court size	: single 13.4 × 5.2 m (44 × 17 ft)
	: double 13.4 × 6.1 m (44 × 20 ft)
net height	: 1.55 m (5 ft 1 in)
scoring	: 15-point game, best of 3 or 5 (men); 11-point game, best of 3 (women)

Baseball

number in team	: 9
size	: side of diamond 27.4 m (90 ft), pitching distance 18.4 m (60 ft 6 in)
length of bat	: 1.07 m (3 ft 6 in) maximum
ball	: weight 142–156 g (5–5.5 oz)
duration of game	: 9 innings minimum, winner with greatest number of home runs

Basketball

number in team	: 5
size of court	: 26 × 14 m (85 × 46 ft)
baskets	: height 3 m (10 ft), diameter 45.7 cm (1.5 ft)
ball	: weight 600–650 g (21–23 oz)
duration of game	: 40 minutes playing time (2 × 20 sessions) plus 5-minute sessions until one side has scored greatest number of goals

Billiards

size of table	: 3.66 × 1.87 m (12 × 6 ft 1.5 in)
billiard balls	: red, white, spot white
scoring	: pot or in–off 3, white 2, cannon 2

Bobsleigh

number in team	: 2 or 4
length of course	: 1500 m (1640 yds) minimum, 15 banked turns
duration	: shortest aggregate time after 4 descents

Bowls

number of players	: singles (4 bowls each, 21 shots up)
	: pairs (2–4 bowls each, 21 ends)
	: triples (2 or 3 bowls each, 18 ends)
	: fours (2 bowls each, 21 ends)
green	: 40.2 × 5.8 m (132 × 19 ft) maximum
bowls	: weight 1.59 kg (3.5 lbs) maximum; diameter 14.6 cm (5.75 in) maximum
jack	: weight 227–284 g (8–10 oz), diameter 6.35 cm (2.5 in)

Boxing

size of ring	: professional 4.27 × 4.27 m (14 × 14 ft) minimum 6.10 × 6.10 m (20 × 20 ft) maximum; amateur 3.66 × 3.66 (12 × 12 ft) minimum, 4.88 × 4.88 m (16 × 16 ft) maximum
weight of gloves	: professional, up to welterweight 170 g (6 oz)
	: light middleweight upwards 227 g (8 oz)
	: amateur 227 g (8 oz)

Weights

Weights		Maximum Weight kg	lbs
light flyweight	professional	48.99	108
	amateur	47.63	105
flyweight	professional	50.80	112
	amateur	50.80	112
super flyweight	professional	52.16	115
	amateur	52.16	115
bantamweight	professional	53.53	118
	amateur	53.98	119
light featherweight	professional	55.34	122
	amateur	55.34	122
featherweight	professional	57.15	126
	amateur	57.15	126
junior lightweight	professional	58.97	130
	amateur	—	—
lightweight	professional	61.24	135
	amateur	60.33	133
welterweight	professional	66.68	147
	amateur	67.13	148
light middleweight	professional	69.63	135.5
	amateur	69.63	135.5
middleweight	professional	72.58	160
	amateur	72.84	165
light heavyweight	professional	79.38	175
	amateur	80.74	178
cruiserweight	professional	86.18	190
	amateur	—	—
heavyweight	professional	no limit	
	amateur	no limit	

Cricket

number in team	: 11, substitutes allowed only for fielding, but runner permitted for injured batsman
wicket length	: 20 m (22 yds)
bat	: length 96.5 cm (38 in) maximum, width 10.8 cm (4.25 in)

ball : weight 156–163 g (5.5–
5.75 oz)

Croquet

number of players	: 2 or 4
size of court	: 32 × 25.6 m (35 × 28 yds)
ball	: weight 454 g (1 lb), diameter 9.2 cm (3.725 in)

Curling

number in team	: 4
rink	: 42 × 4.28 m (138 × 14 ft)
targets (houses)	: diameter 3.66 m (12 ft)
stones	: weight 20 kg (44 lb), circumference 91.4 cm (36 in), preferably made of granite
duration	: 10–12 ends (heads) or time limit

Fencing

events	: epée (men), foil, sabre (men)
duration of bout	: first to achieve 5 hits or 6 minutes (men)
	: first to achieve 4 hits or 5 minutes (women)

Football, American

number in team	: 11, substitutes with maximum 40 in team
size of pitch	: 110 × 49 m (360 × 160 ft)
goals	: height 6 m (20 ft), width 5.6 m (18.5 ft)
ball	: length 28 cm (11 in), weight 397–425 g (14–15 oz)
scoring	: touchdown 6 points, extra point 1 point, safety 2 points, field goal 3 points

Football, Association

number in team	: 11, 2 substitutes allowed
size of pitch	: 120 × 91 m (130 × 100 yds) maximum
ball	: weight 396–493 g (14–16 oz), circumference 68–71 cm (27–28 in)
duration	: 90 minutes (2 × 45 minute sessions); 2 × 15 minutes extra time, if scores equal

Football, Australian

number in team	: 18, 2 substitutes allowed
size of pitch	: oval 185 × 155 m (202 × 170 yds) maximum
ball	: weight 454–482 g (16–17 oz)
scoring	: goal 6 points, behind goal 1 point
duration	: 100 minutes (4 × 25-minute sessions)

Football, Gaelic

number in team	: 15, 3 substitutes allowed
size of pitch	: 146 × 91 m (160 × 100 yds) maximum
goal posts	: height of cross bar 2.4 m (8 ft)
ball	: weight 370–425 g (13–15 oz), circumference 69–74 g (13–15 oz)
scoring	: goal 3 points, ball over crossbar 1 point
duration	: 60 minutes (2 × 30 minute sessions)

Golf

number of players	: singles, pairs, fours
ball	: weight 46g (1.62 oz)

	(maximum)
hole	: diameter 10.8 cm (4.25 in)
terminology	: par = standard score for the hole
	: double bogey = 2 over par
	: bogey = 1 over par
	: birdie = 1 under par
	: eagle = 2 under par

Gymnastics

| events | : floor exercises, horizontal bar, parallel bars, pommel horse, rings, lengthwise vault (men), asymmetrical bars, beam, floor exercises to music, vault (women) |

Handball

number in team	: 7, substitutes allowed, maximum in team 12
size of court	: 44 × 22 m (144 × 72 ft) maximum
goals	: width 3 m (9.8 ft), height 2 m (6.6 ft)
ball	: weight 475 g (16.75 oz) maximum (men), 400 g (14 oz) maximum (women); circumferernce 60 cm (24 in) maximum (men), 56 cm (22 in) maximum (women)
duration	: 60 minutes (2 × 30 minute sessions) men, 50 minutes (2 × 25 minute sessions) women; tournaments 2 × 15 minute sessions (men), 2 × 10 minute sessions (women) without the customary 10 minute interval

Hockey

number in team	: 11, 2 substitutes allowed in men's hockey
size of pitch	: 91.4 × 54.9 m (100 × 80 yds)
goals	: width 3.66 m (12 ft), height 2.13 m (7 ft)
ball	: weight 163 g (5.75 oz) maximum, circumference 23 cm (9 in) maximum
duration	: 70 minutes (2 × 35 minute sessions)

Ice Hockey

number in team	: 6, substitutes allowed with maximum of 17 in team
size of rink	: 61 × 30.5 m (200 × 100 ft) maximum
surround of rink	: high boards 1.22 m (4 ft) maximum
goal	: 1.83 × 1.22 m (6 × 4 ft)
puck	: weight 170 g (6 oz) maximum, diameter 7.6 cm (3 in), thickness 2.5 cm (1 in)
duration	: 60 minutes (3 × 20 minute sessions)

Ice Skating

speed skating events	: 500 m, 1000 m (women), 1500 m, 3000 m (women), 5000 m (men), 10,000 m (men)
figure skating events	: individual men, individual women, pairs, ice-dancing pairs
scoring	: 2 sets of marks are given for technical merit and for artistic impression

Lacrosse

number in team	: 10, 12 (women)
size of pitch	: 100 × 64 m (110 × 70 yds) maximum
goals	: 1.8 × 1.8 m Z(6 × 6 ft)
ball	: weight 142 g (5 oz) maximum, circumference 20.3 cm (8 in) maximum
duration	: 60 minutes (4 × 15 minute sessions) men, 50 minutes (2 × 25 minute sessions) women

Netball

number in team	: 7, substitutes allowed for injuries
size of court	: 30.5 × 15.2 (100 × 50 ft)
net	: height 3.05 m (10 ft), diameter 38 cm (15 in)
duration	: 60 minutes (4 × 15 minute sessions)

Riding

show jumping	: events vary, but speed and ability to negotiate courses and heights of jumps included
three-day events	: dressage, cross-country and show jumping

Rugby, League

number in team	: 13, 2 substitutes allowed
size of pitch	: 100 × 69 m (110 × 75 yds) maximum between goals
	: 11 m (12 yds) maximum behind goals
goals	: cross bar 3 m (10 ft), width 5.6 m (18.5 ft)

ball	: very slightly smaller than Rugby Union ball
scoring	: try 4 points, conversion 2 points, dropped goal 2 points (only 1 in internationals), penalty 2 points
duration	: 80 minutes (2 × 40 minute sessions)

Rugby, Union

number in team	: 15, 2 substitutes allowed in internationals
size of pitch	: 100 × 69 m (110 × 75 yds) maximum between goals
	: 23 m (25 yds) behind goals
goals	: crossbar 3 m (10 ft), width 5.6 m (18.5 ft)
ball	: weight 425 g (15 oz) maximum, length 28 cm (11 in), short circumference 65 cm (25.5 in) maximum
scoring	: try 4 points, conversion 2 points, penalty goal 3 points, dropped goal 3 points

Skiing, Alpine

| downhill events | : vertical drop 1,000 m (3,281 ft) maximum (men), 700 m (2,297 ft) maximum (women) |
| slalom | : 75 gates maximum (men), 60 gates maximum (women) |

Skiing, Nordic

| distance events | : 5 km (3.1 miles) women, 10 km (6.2 miles) women, 15 km (9.3 miles) men, 30 km |

(18.6 miles) men, 50 km (31 miles) men

relays	: 4 × 10 km (men), 3 × 5 km (women)
Nordic combination	: 15 km cross-country; 70 and 90 m (230 and 295 feet) ski jumping

Snooker

size of table	: 3.66 × 1.87 m (12 × 6 ft 1$\frac{1}{2}$ in)
balls	: diameter 5.2 cm (2$\frac{1}{16}$ in)
values of balls	: black 7 points, pink 6 points, blue 5 points, brown 4 points, green 3 points, yellow 2 points, red (15) each worth 1 point

Squash

number of players	: 2
size of court	: side walls 8.75 × 6.40 m (32 ft × 21 ft), front wall height 4.57 m (15 ft)
ball	: weight 24.6 g (0.87 oz) maximum, diameter 41.5 mm (1.63 in) maximum
racket	: length 68.6 cm (27 in) maximum
scoring	: 9 up games, best of 5

Swimming and diving

Standard Olympic swimming pool: length 50 m, 8 lanes

Swimming	Distance
freestyle	: 100 m, 200 m, 400 m, 800 m (women), 1,500 m (men)
backstroke	: 100 m, 200 m
breaststroke	: 100 m, 200 m
butterfly	: 100 m, 200 m

medley	: 200 m (butterfly, backstroke, breaststroke and freestyle legs)
relays	: 4 × 100 freestyle, 4 × 200 freestyle, 4 × 100 m medley (backstroke, breaststroke, butterfly and freestyle legs)

Diving   **Height**

high board	: 3 m, 5 m, 7.5 m, 10 m
springboard	: 1 m, 3 m
competition dives	
high board	: 4 with maximum difficulty of 7.5, 6 others (men); 4 with maximum difficulty of 7.5, 4 others (women)
springboard	: 5 required dives, 6 chosen dives (men); 5 required dives, 5 chosen dives (women)

Table tennis

number of players	: 2 or 4
size of table	: 2.74 × 1.56 m (9 × 5 ft), 76 cm (2.5 ft) high
net	: 15.2 cm (6.08 in) high
ball	: weight 2.53 g (0.089 oz) maximum, diameter 38 mm (1.5 in) maximum
scoring	: 21 point game, best of 3 or 5 games

Tennis

number of players	: 2 or 4
size of court	: single 23.77 × 8.23 m (78 × 27 ft), double 23.77 × 10.97 m (78 × 36 ft)
ball	: weight 58.9 g (2.063 oz) maximum, diameter 6.67 cm (2.625 oz) maximum

net : height 91.4 cm (3 ft)

racket : no limit to size, but maximum weight approximately 400 g (14 oz)

scoring : 4 point game, best of 3 or 5 6-game sets with winner leading by 2 points, games or sets; tie-breakers in operation when games reach 6–6 or 8–8 except in final set

Volleyball

number in team : 6, 6 substitutes allowed

size of court : 18 × 9 m (59 × 29.5 ft)

net : height 2.43 m (7 ft 11.7 in) men, 2.21 m (7 ft 3 in), women

ball : weight 280 g (10 oz) maximum, circumference 67 cm (26.4 in) maximum

scoring : 15 point sets, best of 3 or 5 sets

Water polo

number in team : 7, 4 substitutes allowed

size of pool : 30 m × 20 m (99 × 66 ft) maximum; depth 1 m (3.28 ft) minimum, 1.8 m (5.9 ft) for internationals

goal : 3 × 0.9 m (9.75 × 3 ft)

ball : weight 450 g (16 oz) maximum, circumference 71 cm (28 in) maximum

duration : 20 minutes (4 × 5 minute sessions)

Water Skiing

events : figures (freestyle tricks), jumping, slalom

Weightlifting

Types of lift (Olympic)

clean and jerk : bar raised to shoulders; as legs are straightened, bar pushed up with straight arms

snatch : bar raised over head with straightened arms in one movement

Non-Olympic lifts: dead lift, bench press, squat

Weights	Maximum Weight	
	kg	lbs
flyweight	52	114.5
bantamweight	56	123.25
featherweight	60	132.25
lightweight	67.5	148.75
middleweight	75	165.25
light heavyweight	82.5	181.75
middle heavyweight	90	198.25
heavyweight	110	242.50
super heavyweight	no limit	no limit

Indoor games

Cards

number in normal pack : usually 52 cards, 2 jokers, 4 suits each of 13 cards

number in Tarot pack (used for fortune telling) : 78

Chess

board : chequered, 64 squares

| | alternating in 2 colours |
| chessmen | : 1 king, 1 queen, 2 rooks (castles), 2 bishops, 2 knights, 8 pawns for each player |

Darts

| board | : 45 cm (18 in) in diameter, divided into 20 segments, two circles; outer circle = 25 score, inner circle (bull) = 50 score |
| darts | : usually 16 cm (6 in) long, weights vary |

Dice

| dice | : cube numbered on each face from 1–6; spots on opposite faces always totalling 7, e.g. 4 is opposite 3 |

Dominoes

| blocks | : 28 rectangular blocks with white dots numbering 1–6 on one side only |

Draughts

| board | : chequered, 64 squares alternating in 2 colours |
| counters | : black and white, 16 for each player |

<u>Notes</u>

<u>Notes</u>

Notes

<u>**Notes**</u>

<u>Notes</u>

<u>Notes</u>